CAREGIVERS
BIBLE

MANAGING BEHAVIOR PROBLEMS IN THE ELDERLY

William Cone, Ph.D.

Cover Design by William Cone
Text design by Paul Matteson

ISBN 0-9655563-0-1

First Edition, December 1997
Second edition January   2004

Printed in the United States of America
10 9 8 7 6 5 4 3 2

Matteson Books
16707 Sunset Boulevard
Pacific Palisades, CA 90272

CAREGIVERS
BIBLE

MANAGING BEHAVIOR
PROBLEMS
IN THE ELDERLY

William Cone, PhD

MATTESON BOOKS
16707 Sunset Boulevard
Pacific Palisades, CA 90272
(888)-261-0576

*"How far you go in life depends on you being
tender with the young,
compassionate with the aged,
sympathetic with the striving,
and tolerant of the weak and the strong.
Because someday in life,
you will have been all of these."*

George Washington Carver (1864-1943)

"Age is of no importance unless you are a cheese."

Billie Burke (1886-1970)

CONTENTS

*See page
152 - Rating of Caregiving
Activities*

SECTION THREE: MANAGING BEHAVIOR PROBLEMS

Section One

CARING FOR AN AGING AMERICA

Chapter one

AGEISM

During the year after World War II ended, fifteen million soldiers suddenly came home. This rush of returning young men and women resulted in an explosive rise in our population, and spawned the generation now known as the *baby boomers*.

During the next several decades, while the boomers were growing up, breakthroughs in sanitation, nutrition, and medicine led to an unanticipated increase in life expectancy, and an unprecedented increase in the number of elder Americans.

The baby boomers, and their parents, are getting old. In the decades ahead, millions of these aging Americans will face the need for health care. But our youth oriented society has not prepared itself to deal with this rapidly growing segment of the population.

As well as dealing with the normal problems of aging, elderly people in our country come face-to-face with another problem—the bias and prejudice we have developed against growing old.

Behavioral Objectives

At the end of this section, participants will be able to:

Understand the meaning and consequences of age bias in the treatment setting

Describe emotional reactions in working with the elderly

Take steps to improve the well being of older people in need of care

Describe the factors contributing to agism in our culture

Since the end of the war, the United States has been evolving into a culture of youth. Age is out—youth is in.

The cosmetic surgery business is exploding. Bookstores are bursting with books on how to reverse the aging process. Each day, two hundred cable channels are choked with infomercials spewing promises of eternal youth and fitness.

And so we are taught by our culture and our media to devalue and denigrate aging. Our language is replete with derogatory terms like, "over-the-hill," "geezer," "old coot," and, "old biddy."

For the last few decades our television programs and movies have romanticized youth and devalued age. For example, in the movie *Logan's Run*, all citizens were mandated to end their lives when they reached thirty. Our cultural heroes never grow old-after all these years, Superman and Barbie have never gained a pound or a wrinkle.

It's no secret that we value our first years more than our last. Today's seventy-five year old may actually live another 25 years, but few of us place much value on those years.

To get an idea of how age bias affects us, imagine the value of giving a 20 year old a new heart that will extend her life another twenty-five years. Now think about performing the same operation on a seventy-five year old. Is it worth the expense? Does someone this old deserve a new heart? Many would say, "No—she's too old, let her die."

This bias is ageism—youth is positive, age is negative. And ageism touches every part of our culture.

Many factors have contributed to the emphasis on

attractiveness, youth, power, and self-centeredness. The baby-boomers are the first generation ever to be reared with the relentless influence of mass-media. They are the first generation in history whose primary source of information was from the media, rather than from their immediate and extended family.

Television, radio, movies, magazines and comics have had an immeasurably profound impact. Rather than relying on the wisdom of their elders, baby-boomers got their information from young, powerful, attractive celebrities. As technology outpaced the average person's ability to assimilate it, the wisdom of the elders became less valuable and less useful. Older people came to be seen as a liability rather than an asset. During the seventies, "Don't trust anyone over thirty," and, "I hope I die before I get old," became the favorite cries of the youth generation

In the mid 1900s, retirement became the norm among blue-collar workers. For the first time, older workers were forced out and replaced with younger people. Experience became less valuable than youth.

As well as being media children, baby-boomers have enjoyed extended and privileged childhoods. Although most of us don't realize it, it was during the boomers' school years that adolescence came to be seen as the latter part of childhood, rather than the early part of adulthood. Kids grew up more slowly, and left home later.

After World War II, programs like the GI bill and generous government loans enabled thousands of middleclass people to attend college, which delayed their entry into the work force.

During the fifties, more people bought homes than in

any time in history. A new type of neighborhood—the suburb—emerged, and led to another unprecedented phenomenon—the two car family. These events led to the American obsession with conspicuous consumption.

It was during this time that consumption replaced achievement as the hallmark of success. The high level of prosperity and the mass promotion by the media of the obtainability of the much publicized American Dream created very high—and sometimes unrealistic—expectations in an entire generation.

The soap-operas of the late forties and early fifties bore titles like, *Right to Happiness,* and *Life can be Beautiful.* Baby-boomers and their parents were taught that they should expect to have their every need met. Taking, rather than giving, became the new mind set.

These factors are vitally important today, because the baby-boom generation is now aging, and is also faced with caring for aging parents.

Only a few generations ago the extended family was the norm. Several generations often lived in one house. Age was seen as synonymous with wisdom. Children were taught to revere and respect their elders, and Grandpa was truly grand. People grew, aged, and died at home.

But today's family is more mobile—the average family moves once every ten years. Friends and relatives are left behind, and the sense of family and community has dwindled.

As a culture that expects to have its needs met and its problems solved, we have increasingly come to depend on others for solutions. This is the era of the expert. The consultant has replaced the cowboy and the troubleshooter has replaced the six-shooter. The result of this is the tendency of the children of aging parents to reject the job of caring for parents and, with high expectations, turn over the responsibility to the health care community. At the same time, their investment in eternal youth and power gives them an unrealistic view of what medicine can do.

Many of today's children—rather than feeling a sense of compassion and devotion to their parents—react to the deterioration of their once healthy and productive progenitors as an intolerable, narcissistic injury. Watching parents age reminds the youth-forever generation of their own mortality, and this induces unpleasant thoughts and feelings. For these people, caring for aging parents is felt to be a burden that should obviously be shouldered by someone else.

Those who cannot cope with the loss of their narcissistic, youth-forever fantasies blame outside forces for their problems. Instead of recognizing age as an inevitable part of life, they blame the health care industry for failing to fix what they fear. Projection and blame become the chosen methods of coping. This blame is often projected onto the people who are caring for their parents. While they may shun their responsibility, they are often quick to criticize, eager to oversee, and unable to understand the scope of the task they have handed over to the care givers. It is important to keep this in mind when dealing with families—it is not their anger, but their fear that speaks so loudly.

The impact of all of these forces, combined with the high expectations of caregivers themselves, has created a predisposition in the elderly to see themselves as bitter and helpless victims of the forces around them.

CARE GIVERS BIBLE

Healthcare professionals are not immune to this bias. Without realizing it, some care givers infantilize, demean, and talk down to their elderly clients. Exposed each day to the wizened and weathered face of age, they become reactive rather than responsive. Constantly confronted with the very thing they so strongly wish to avoid, some actually come to hate those whom they had so earnestly pledged to help.

And because of this negative reaction to age, many elderly people have come to devalue themselves. Like the youth who look upon the aged with disdain, the elderly often see themselves as useless, used up, and in the way. Confronted with rejection and infantilization older people are prone to lose their feeling of power, their sense of worth, and their feeling of lovability— the three basic components of self-esteem.

This negative self-deprecating perception often lays the groundwork for depression, withdrawal, and deterioration.

Age bias is a cause of many of the difficulties in term care facilities. One of the best examples of age bias I have seen appears in Nancy Wexler's book, *Mama Can't Remember Anymore*. In the book, Paul E. Ruskin, M.D. explains,

"I was invited to present a lecture to a class of graduate nurses who were studying the "Psychological Aspects of Aging" I started my lecture with the following case presentation:

'The patient is a white female who appears her reported age. She neither speaks nor comprehends the spoken word. Sometimes she babbles incoherently for hours on end. She is disoriented about person, place and time. She does, however, seem to recognize her own name. I have worked with her

6

for the past six months, but she still doesn't recognize me.

She shows complete disregard for her physical appearance and makes no effort whatsoever to assist in her own care. She must be fed, bathed and clothed by others. Because she is toothless, her food must be pureed; because she is incontinent of both urine and stool, she must be changed and bathed often. Her shirt is generally soiled from almost constant drooling. She does not walk. Her sleep pattern is erratic.

Often, she awakens in the middle of the night, and her screaming awakens others. Most of the time she is very friendly and happy. However, several times a day she gets quite agitated without apparent cause. Then she screams loudly until someone comes to comfort her.'

After the case presentation, I asked the nurses how they would feel about taking care of a patient as the one described. They used words such as, frustrated," "hopeless," "depressed," and "annoyed" to describe how they would feel.

When I stated that I enjoyed taking care of her and that I thought they would too, the class looked at me in disbelief. I then passed around a picture of the patient: my six-month-old daughter.

After the laughter had subsided, I asked why it was so much more difficult to care for a ninety year-old patient, than a six-month-old with identical symptoms.

We all agreed that it's physically easier to take care of a helpless baby weighing 15 pounds than a helpless adult weighing 100 pounds, but the answer seemed to go deeper than this.

The infant, we all decided, represents new life, hope, and almost infinite potential. The demented senior citizen, on the other hand, represents the end of life with little potential for growth. We need to change our perspective.

The aged patient is just as lovable as the child. Those who are ending their lives in the vulnerability of old age deserve the same care and attention as those who are beginning their lives in the vulnerability of infancy."

As Ruskin so effectively points out, the solution to these problems is the realization by both care givers and elderly that an older person is still a person; that deference and dignity do not expire when social security begins; that to be old need not be an imposition, but a valuable part of human experience.

This book is dedicated to total quality care giving—the notion that, once we conquer our own demons, we can make caring for the aged a rewarding experience for patient and care giver alike.

Chapter Two

LEAVING HOME

Although most families make heroic efforts to care for their ailing elderly, many eventually are forced to consider moving the person into a professional care facility.

The decision to admit a parent, a spouse, or any family member to a health care facility is difficult and painful. It is usually made when all other alternatives have been exhausted. It is seldom made without guilt, remorse, hurt and anger.

The move from home to a retirement home, assisted living, board & care, or skilled nursing facility is a very difficult transition for both resident and family.

To the family, it means the loss of much of what has become familiar. They must adjust to living without their loved one. They must grapple with the reality that they are not equipped to give adequate care. They must lick their wounds and learn their limitations.

To the person entering the professional care facility, it means dealing with multiple losses. She loses her home, her privacy, and her independence. Friends,

Behavioral Objectives

At the end of this section readers will be able to:

Describe the losses associated with relocation

Name the five phases of relocation adjustment

Define relocation stress syndrome

Take steps to reduce the trauma of relocation

9

Symptoms of Relocation Stress Syndrome

• loneliness
• depression
• anger
• apprehension
• anxiety
• sleep disturbance
• changes in eating habits
• increased dependency
• insecurity
• lack of trust
• excessive need for reassurance

treasured objects, lifestyle, and much of what she knew is gone forever. This overwhelming sense of multiple loss is usually accompanied by anxiety, depression and disorientation. In most cases, the stress of transition is temporary, but it sometimes persists, leading to a condition known in psychiatric literature as an *adjustment disorder.*

Although leaving home and entering a care facility is traumatic, relocation from one facility to another also takes its toll on the physical and psychological health of elders.

Residents face an elevated mortality risk whenever they are relocated. In fact, studies of the effect of transferring people have found elevated mortality risk between 1.99 and 3.76 times greater than those patients who were not transferred.

After years of observing and documenting this problem, in 1992, health care experts officially named this phenomenon *Relocation Stress Syndrome.*

The United States Administration on Aging calls this problem *Transfer Trauma,* and notes that relocation is associated with depression, increased irritability, serious illness and elevated mortality risk.

The fear and grief that the person is experiencing are often expressed as anger. While fear disables a person, anger is empowering. To a person who has lost most of her personal power and position, anger and resistance may be the only way to feel one's impact on the world.

Understanding the origin of this anger and resistance allows care givers to reach beyond the anger and gently touch the pain. A kind word and an understanding attitude can make this difficult transition much more bearable.

PREPARING FOR DEPARTURE

The stresses of moving to a care facility were carefully examined by Coffman in 1983. He pointed out that it wasn't the move itself, but the person's perception of the quality of care and the social support they would receive at the facility that was most traumatic. In other words, it wasn't the change itself but the emotions that surrounded that change that made the event difficult.

Coffman also found that moves that were carefully planned, were carried out with adequate warning, and included consultation with the person, had far better outcome.

Things went best when the person was given information far in advance of the move. Allowing them to visit the facility several times and giving them the opportunity to get to know the staff before the move permitted the person to enter an environment that was familiar, with a staff whom they already knew.

PLANNING FOR ARRIVAL

Planning effective care giving and behavioral management involves several important steps. Careful implementation of each of these steps results in more satisfaction for both resident and staff.

1. Get a thorough history and physical, and description of any existing problems before the person arrives.

Find out everything you can about the person, and inform the staff what to expect.

2. Based on the information available, establish the apparent cause of any existing

behavior problems.

Be aware that behavioral problems may be caused by physical illness, mental illness, environmental stressors, and medication problems.

3. Establish a preliminary intervention plan based on the information you have been given.

Remember that this person has been brought to your facility usually because he or she has decompensated, is experiencing acute medical or behavioral problems, is gravely disabled, or has become too difficult to care for in his or her previous location. This means that a good number of people arrive already exhibiting disruptive behavior that must be managed immediately.

4. Do not put a new person in the proximity of others until a medical assessment, a behavioral assessment, and observation of the person's capacity to interact has been done.

The presence of a new person is often disruptive to other residents. New residents may also be combative, explosive, and potentially dangerous to others.

5. Establish a structured daily care, social activity, and free time schedule so that the day is predictable.

These routines should be shared with all staff members. They should also be posted in the person's room and should be told to the resident several times.

6. Schedule sessions of physical activity to match the person's energy cycle.

7. Provide rest periods each day when the

person can listen to music, sit in a recliner, and take naps if appropriate.

8. Monitor the use of visual and hearing aids. Help the resident establish a routine of using these devices.

9. Assign a specific person to be the primary care giver so that rapport can be established.

10. Assign the minimum number of staff necessary to a specific resident.

11. Minimize isolation and idle time.

Isolation leads to decompensation, and idle time increases self-stimulating behavior.

LABELING

New environments are confusing. Careful organization of the environment can significantly reduce confusion, disorientation, and unwanted behaviors, and make it easier to correct those that do occur.

As well as being upset and disoriented, a significant number of people entering long-term care facilities will exhibit signs of depression, dementia, or other cognitive problems.

People with dementia will have great difficulty storing and retrieving new information from their long term memory, so orientation, instructions, and directions are soon forgotten. Furthermore, many residents can no longer read, because they can no longer see or comprehend written words.

1. Clearly label objects and the location of stored objects.

Signs are easier to see if the background is dark and

the symbol light, rather than a light background with dark symbols. Blues and greens should be avoided because those colors are difficult for older people to see.

2. Use large, high contrast, pictures when possible—not written instructions.

Make sure that the person can understand the meaning of the picture—ask them to tell you what it means.

3. Use pictures or objects that remind residents of where they are, where important locations are, and what they are to do in the locations.

For example, putting the resident's picture on the door to his room will remind him where it is, while putting a picture of a knife & fork on the cafeteria door reminds him where to eat.

For residents with more advanced dementia, use pictures of them that were taken before they began to suffer from the disorder. Many people with dementia do not recognize pictures of themselves that were taken after the symptoms began.

3. Use multiple labels.

For example, put a rest-room label with a direction arrow in the hall and put another label on the restroom door.

4. Place all labels where they can be seen from a wheelchair.

5. Fasten a brightly colored ribbon to the door knob of the person's room, and put a ribbon of the same color on the person's wrist—he can find the room by matching the

ribbons.

PREPARE A SAFE ENVIRONMENT

Keep the environment clean and simple, with as few distractions as possible. The residents' short attention span and difficulty processing information makes complex stimuli incomprehensible and disturbing.

1. Minimize the use of intercoms, televisions buzzers, bells, and other noises.

Many residents become frightened by these noises. Those suffering from psychotic disorders may incorporate these sounds into their delusions

2. Place residents that are confused by too much stimulation in small groups.

Avoid putting them in large, noisy, multi-purpose rooms. They may become over-stimulated and agitated.

3. Remove unnecessary mirrors, confusing signs, complicated wallpaper and bedding with complex patterns.

Demented or psychotic people often get caught up in the patterns, which can become the source of hallucinations.

4. Put residents who are disturbed by noise in quiet rooms. Check the room yourself to monitor the noise level.

Find out which rooms are the noisiest. At one facility the staff members volunteered to spend the night in each of the rooms.

By doing this it was discovered that several of the rooms were too noisy to sleep in, and that one room was situated across from the nurses station in such a way that the light from the station shined directly on the bed. Putting the staff in the resident's rooms for a night gave them a first hand appreciation for the light and noise level found in each room.

MINIMIZE DANGER

Because newly arrived residents are often frail, confused, unfamiliar with the surroundings, and may be on medication, they have a high risk of falling or hurting themselves.

Those with dementia are at even higher risk because they are unable to recognize potential dangers in their environment. Their judgement is impaired, and their vision and depth perception may be poor. Therefore,

1. Remove furniture and any other objects with sharp edges.

Keep furniture and other equipment in good condition. Loose parts and exposed edges are potential sources of injury.

2. Remove any spoiled food or other substances that could be accidentally swallowed.

3. Carefully monitor smoking, and restrict it to certain areas.

4. Use ample non-glare lighting. Use night lights in all rooms.

5. Reduce the glare from shiny floors and other polished surfaces.

6. Put all beds in a low position when unattended.

7. Remove all trash and other clutter frequently.

8. Make sure clothing is on properly.

Especially take note of shoes—see that they are on properly and tied.

9. Make sure all personal items are stored in a safe place.

PERSONALIZE THE ENVIRONMENT

Every person has the need for personal space. When residents enter a hospital or care facility, they lose any sense of personal territory. They often must share rooms with strangers, and previously personal space such as bathrooms and eating areas are no longer available. Arguing and fighting often occur because of disagreements about personal space.

1. Ask the family to bring inexpensive personal belongings and to help decorate the person's room with them.

Include as many personal items in the environment as possible.

2. Make an inventory of the items so that both staff and family are aware of what is in the room.

3. Mark all personal belongings with identification.

4. When possible and practical, fasten the personal belongings to the wall or furniture, so that they cannot be lost or stolen.

5. Make it pleasant

Odors like cleaning supplies, deodorants, sanitizing sprays, and substances designed to mask other unpleasant odors, are often overpowering. On the other hand, the smell of cooking, flowers, newly mowed lawn, or even outdoor air are experiences that people in institutions may rarely have an opportunity to experience.

Common sights such as trees, sounds such as birds singing, and fragrances like coffee perking may be absent from the older person's environment. Providing opportunities to enjoy these everyday pleasures greatly enriched the quality of life.

Chapter three

FAMILIES

Interactions with family members are an important part of every care plan. At best, the family can be a valuable resource. They can provide historical information and furnish data on what types of care giving have been most successful in the past. They also provide a powerful source of comfort and support for the resident.

But at other times, families may present problems. In many cases the family members have become accustomed to being the primary care givers, and are over-involved with the patient. Although they mean well, they may disagree with care giving, and sometimes actually interfere with treatment.

According to J. Paul Teusnik, M.D. and Susan Mahler, M.S.W., families of elderly patients with progressive cognitive decline undergo a step-wise process in attempting to cope with the disorder—they feel that families coping with debilitating disease exhibit similar reactions to families coping with death.

Behavioral Objectives

At the end of this section readers will be able to

Describe the five stages of coping with cognitive decline

Explain the function of denial and minimizing of a family member's illness

Use constructive methods to help family members deal with their concerns

Effectively involve family in the treatment regimen

Because of this, care givers should provide the families with information and education about this process so that they can see that what they are feeling is normal. With support and guidance, a family can successfully work through their reactions and be able to mourn the loss of their loved one, make the necessary decisions for her care, and re-establish a new family equilibrium.

DENIAL

At first, family members may notice memory and behavioral problems in their loved one, but explain them away by saying that they are just "stress," or part of getting old. They insist that there is nothing wrong with their loved one in spite of the evidence. This reaction is sometimes the result of the family's lack of education about aging, but it is also a wish on the part of family members to deny what they are seeing.

Denial is a way of defending against the pain of loss. In addition, the frequent family fights about how to handle the loved one's illness may actually be a way for the family to postpone dealing with their grief. In these cases, denial makes any objective assessment, decision making, treatment planning difficult.

Families who exhibit excessive denial must be helped through education and at times through outright confrontation—to recognize the extent of the disability of their family member. Although this may lead to further anger, it is only when denial is overcome that they will be able to make sound decisions and realistic plans for treatment.

OVER-INVOLVEMENT

Denial is often followed by intense over-involvement of family members with the patient, in an attempt to deal with the illness.

As the deterioration of the afflicted family member becomes more obvious, family members may take over daily tasks and responsibilities in an effort to compensate for the deficits.

At this point, a role reversal takes place. Frequently the family member must almost become a parent to his or her own parent. This can be one of the most difficult adjustments that families must face. In addition, they often must assume the patient's former family role, which may include taking over legal and financial responsibilities. This task can be difficult and stressful. Occasionally, family fights break out about who is to take on this responsibility. Sibling rivalry re-emerges.

In many cases a child must take on this role even if the patient's spouse is still living. Tasks and responsibilities that were done by one spouse for many decades are sometimes incomprehensible to the non-ailing partner. For example, some wives have never written a check or paid a bill, and, in combination with the stress of dealing with illness in their spouse, find the task overwhelming.

When involvement with a parent becomes an obsession, family members sacrifice their personal lives and become consumed with the care giving task. Even when they recognize that they are in over their heads, they may be reluctant to seek professional help, thinking that to do so is to betray their parent.

In fact, some families raise sons or daughters to believe that they must care for their parents regardless of how disruptive it may be to their own lives. The children feel that to not do so will result in ostracism and ridicule by their family, and their community. This belief often stretches them to the breaking point.

In these cases the person must be helped to understand what is within their power to do, and what is beyond their limits.

Professional care givers should be able to recognize the difference between a normal reaction and over involvement within the family and its culture. Families must be helped to see that their over-involvement is actually a hindrance rather than a help in top-quality care giving.

When doing this, provide the family members with solid evidence of what problems the over-involvement is causing for the patient, the staff, and for the rest of the family.

ANGER

Eventually, over-involved family members react in anger, feeling unable to shoulder the tremendous burden of caring for their loved one.

Anger among family members develops for many reasons. In addition to the burden of caring for a disabled spouse or parent, they cannot tolerate the bizarre and socially inappropriate behavior their loved one is exhibiting. Anger also can erupt from the feeling of having been abandoned by a still-living but now helpless parent or spouse.

Regardless of its source, this anger is often projected or displaced onto the very people who are trying to help the family deal with their overwhelming sense of helplessness—the care-giving professionals.

Professionals must be able to recognize this, and help

the family confront and deal with their anger. When families fail to see that they are projecting their own painful feelings on caregivers, they often accuse staff of neglecting the patient and causing the deterioration that, in reality, naturally occurs with this illness.

Since the normal reaction to being accused of neglect is defensiveness or anger, either of which will further alienate the families, care givers must be able to handle this anger effectively.

GUILT

As anger lessens, guilt may become more obvious. Feelings of guilt can be a normal reaction to recognizing the feelings of anger. Guilt may also come from unexpressed an unacceptable wishes that their suffering loved one die.

Family members may feel guilty for believing they waited too long before seeking professional help—and by doing so have contributed to the suffering. Guilt can also come from the need to make medical and financial decisions that are objected to by the elderly person.

Guilt may also be the re-awakening of old feelings—feelings that they were not attentive enough to their parent or spouse in earlier times—or for abrasive and cruel comments from times passed.

Family members often mix their guilt with a dash of failure. They have tried their best to care for their loved one, but the task was more than they could bear. It is vital to keep this in mind when dealing with family members. You cannot truly understand their pain until you have walked in their shoes. In these cases, support groups can be a great resource for families who have been struggling with an ailing elder.

Unfortunately, this guilt sometimes gets translated into a need to dictate orders to the staff and care givers. They confuse interference with involvement. One such case involved Jim Stevens and his father.

Jim Stevens brought his father to the nursing home because caring for his dad was disrupting his job to the degree that he was at risk of being fired.

He told the administrator that he wanted to be notified of any and every problem his father was experiencing. He made it clear that no treatment of any kind was to be administered to his father without his approval.

In reality, Mr. Stevens was very difficult to reach. He seldom returned phone calls, and sometimes could not be reached at all. This resulted in impeding any semblance of quality care.

The administrator invited Mr. Stevens to a meeting and said, "Mr. Stevens, I know you care for your father a great deal. I know you worry about him. And we are all impressed with your concern and your involvement. It is true that you want the absolute best for your dad, isn't it?"

"Of course," he replied.

"Well the absolute best care we can give requires immediate intervention at times. If we have to wait, your father may suffer unnecessarily. You wouldn't want to stand in the way of helping him, would you?"

"No. Of course not," he said.

"Then I guess we both agree that when we cannot reach you, we should do what we feel is in your father's best interest, right?"

"I suppose so," he said.

"Great," She said, "then I would like you to sign this agreement stating that if we cannot reach you within an hour, we can do what is best for him."

In this interchange several things happened:

• The administrator *validated* Mr. Steven's feelings and concerns.

• She got him to agree that the *best care* was the most important issue.

• She got him to agree, *in writing*, that they could proceed with treatment if they could not reach him. This assured that there would be no misunderstanding.

Health care professionals can most effectively deal with the family members' guilt by discovering its cause, and taking corrective steps to alleviate it.

One step can be simply to educate the family about the illness itself, thereby providing reassurance that the family has not harmed the patient. More extensive counseling may be needed to help the family make difficult but necessary decisions, some of which may be objected to by the patient.

ACCEPTANCE

Acceptance comes only when a family is able to truly understand the disease or disability that is affecting their loved one. Once they have worked through the bulk of their anger and guilt, and have recognized that their loved one is no longer the person they once knew, they can accept the loss.

In cases of dementia, acceptance can be especially difficult. This disease's insidious onset and long, slow progress, give one false hope that things will remain as they are. In addition, the patient's relatively normal appearance during the early stages of the illness makes the problems seem less serious than they really are.

Here's an example of these problems in a case described by Teusnik and Mahler:

Mrs. K, a profoundly demented 76-year-old Jewish widow, was transferred from a long-term-care facility to the Cornell Medical Center for an evaluation of agitated behavior including constant pacing, verbal abusiveness, and at times combativeness.

Although Mrs. K had exhibited symptoms of Alzheimer's disease for approximately one and a half years, she had worked in her family's garment manufacturing business until one year before her transfer to the center.

In the transfer summary, the nursing home complained of difficulty with the patient's 50-year-old son, who was running his mother's business.

During the initial phase of his mother's hospitalization in our facility, Mr. K was unable to accept his mother's progressive deterioration and was insistent that certain signs, such as intact long-term memory, were proof that she was less impaired than he had been told. He believed that his mother's wandering stemmed from her boredom at not having work to do and from the lack of staff initiating engaging her in activity.

Mr. K visited his mother nightly and brought her dress patterns to cut. When she was unable to perform the tasks he expected of her, he displaced his disappointment and anger onto the nursing staff in a hostile, abusive, and accusatory fashion, thus engendering staff defensiveness and resistance to empathizing with his pain. Mr. K was critical of all aspects of his mother's treatment and expected the hospital to find a miracle cure for her illness.

Engaging Mr. K in family therapy was difficult

since he saw both the doctor and social worker as his adversaries. He was seen in weekly sessions, where he was encouraged to talk about his frustration at our inability to make his mother well.

At the same time, we educated him about Alzheimer's disease—its manifestations, course, and treatment.

Mr. K eventually revealed his concerns that the illness was hereditary or contagious, and his feelings of helplessness in caring for his mother. He had attempted to have her live with his family before placing her in a nursing home, but he and the family were unable to control her wandering and disruption of family life.

As Mr. K began to discuss his family history and his feelings about his mother, it became clear that he had a conflict-ridden, ambivalent relationship with her.

Mrs. K had worked long hours in the family's business since Mr. K was a young child and had left his care to an older sibling. Mr. K had felt neglected and abandoned, and had developed angry feelings toward his mother.

Having to put his mother into a nursing home reawakened these repressed feelings of anger and abandonment, and aroused concerns that he was now abandoning her. He was still unable to see his mother as anything other than the strong, capable, working woman he had known in the past, and although he was capable of running the family business, he was experiencing self-doubts. In addition, he was furious at his sibling, who lived out of town and was not involved with his mother's care.

Mr. K's reminiscences about his mother helped him to realize the source of his angry feelings and he became less critical of the staff.

His lessened anger enabled him to understand the symptoms of Alzheimer's disease, to more realistically assess his mother's illness, and to mourn her loss.

When Mrs. K was discharged from our facility, we talked with the social worker in the long-term care facility where Mrs. K would return, so that we could apprize her of Mr. K's conflicts and encourage her to provide him with continued support.

In other cases, family members have become estranged from the patient, and don't wish to have any involvement at all. In these cases unresolved feelings of anger, frustration, helplessness, grief, and fear interfere with healthy family interaction. Once again, family therapy and family support groups can be very useful.

Unfortunately, in some cases the family members have been not only neglectful, but abusive. In a survey done in 1988, researchers Pfiffer and Finklehor discovered that between 3 and 4 percent of elders experienced abuse by family members. In the majority of cases, the abuser was the patient's spouse. They also discovered that only one in fourteen cases were ever reported.

Social support plays an important part in the potential for abuse. Elderly people who are isolated from all but their caretakers are four times as likely to suffer abuse than those who have social support. Men are more likely to be abused than women, because elderly men seldom live alone.

Regardless of who they are, how they act, and what they have done, family members must always be treated with respect, deference, and consideration. Like the residents, families must be considered to be customers.

FAMILY VISITS

One frequent problem that long term care residents have is loneliness. Most residents complain that families don't visit enough. Although this is sometimes true, in other cases these complaints arise because the resident simply doesn't remember the visits. In these cases making video and tape recordings and taking pictures of the visits is useful.

Unfortunately, family visits can be a source of trouble. Negative interactions with family can irritate and agitate patients. Encourage the family to keep the climate of the visit positive. Explain to them that fighting and friction during a visit can cause behavioral problems for several days.

Family visits can also be an opportunity for patients to complain about the facility and the quality of care. Although some of these complaints may be valid, in many cases the person complains of poor care either because they cannot remember many of the things that are done for them, or because they get pleasure out of stirring up trouble.

Mrs. Whitkin's daughter would visit twice a week. She would arrive at ten o'clock, and spend an hour with her mother. During these visits Mrs. Whitkin would complain incessantly about not being fed, not being cared for, and being generally neglected.

We suggested to her daughter that she come to facility unannounced at different times during the day and stand where her mother could not see her, so that she could observe the things we did for her mother. In this way, she was able to see that we were in fact doing the things that Mrs. Whitkin claimed we did not do. The daughter then realized that much of what we were doing simply forgotten.

BEHAVIORAL INTERVENTIONS TO HELP FAMILY MEMBERS

1. Spend time with the resident's family.

Get to know them, and learn about their expectations, attitudes, and concerns.

2. Acknowledge and validate the feelings and concerns family members are having.

If they are not forthcoming with these feelings, offer information on what kind of feelings are typical and ask them if they are experiencing any of them.

For example, you might say, "It's common for families to feel frightened, depressed, defeated, or guilty about the decision to seek professional help. It would not be unusual for you to be feeling any or all of these things."

3. Family members sometimes express their concern and anxiety as anger.

When this happens, it is very important that you do not internalize a family member's anger. This simply means that you don't take their anger personally. Instead, validate their anger and offer solutions. Be responsive, not reactive. This means instead of getting angry, say, "I can hear that you are very upset. I understand. Let's see what we can do to solve the problem."

4. Tell family members about the resident's current condition.

Carefully explain the symptoms and problems that the resident is experiencing. Explaining problems and unusual behaviors helps the family understand and cope with what they are seeing.

5. Explain how the resident's current condition creates specific needs, and show how these needs can best be met.

6. Explain the facility's policies and procedures.

It is useful to give a written summary of the policies and procedures to all family members, along with a list of answers to the most frequently asked questions, so that there are no misunderstandings about what the facility can and cannot do. Taking the time to make this summary can save hours of explanation later.

7. Involve the family in the care plan whenever possible.

Even minimal participation increases family compliance a great deal. It gives them a feeling of power and participation.

8. Inform them of any change in care plan, and provide the rationale for the change.

9. Inform all staff members of who the family members are, and how they are to be involved in care giving.

10. Inform the family how the quality of the visit effects the quality of life of their relative.

11. Encourage the family to join a support group.

12. Put them in touch with community resources.

Section Two

FACTORS AFFECTING
BEHAVIORAL PROBLEMS

Chapter four

MEMORY PROBLEMS

A great number of emotional and behavioral problems in elderly people are caused by memory difficulties. As memory begins to falter, the person may begin to become anxious and fearful. In the beginning stages of dementia, for example, many people begin to experience anxiety. As they grapple to remember information that once came effortlessly, they begin to fear the worst.

In the early stages of dementia the victim is acutely aware that he is losing his memory. It is not uncommon to hear someone say, "Please help me, I'm afraid that I'm losing my mind."

As the memory loss continues, the person may go into a deep depression. This makes matters even worse, because depression further interferes with memory.

At this point it is vital that the person be screened for depression, and that the depression be treated. Often treating underlying depression results in a significant improvement in memory problems.

Behavioral Objectives

At the end of this section readers will be able to

Describe the consequences of memory impairment

Name the steps in the memory storage process

Assess the memory status of older adults

Describe the differences between short term memory, long term memory, and remote memory

However, many problems that look like memory problems are actually caused by other factors. To understand this, it helps to see how the memory process actually works.

THE MEMORY PROCESS

Although researchers have been exploring memory for many years, no one knows exactly how memories are formed. However, it is known that all information must go through a specific set of steps before it becomes a memory. In addition, a malfunction in any step of the process can be the source of behavioral and emotional problems

INPUT

All memories begin with a stimulus—a source of information that is new to the mind. Most memory stimuli originate from the outside world. For example, every sight, sound, taste, touch and smell is a stimulus.

But memories can also be generated internally by the brain itself, as happens during dreaming, fantasy, thought, creativity, and problem solving. In fact, all of our art, science, and creativity are the end product of generating, synthesizing, and remembering newly formed internal ideas. Many ground-breaking inventions originated from remembering information that was originally generated in dreams.

INPUT PROBLEMS

It's common for people to become less active as they grow older. In general, older people are less physically active, less socially active, and seek out less stimulation.

In fact, many elderly people do very little each day but sit and watch television. They are chronically under-stimulated. These lonely and forgotten people are seldom spoken to, seldom touched, and rarely encouraged to engage in social activity.

The problem is that chronic lack of stimulation greatly accelerates cognitive loss, and it happens quickly. I've seen high functioning people deteriorate within weeks after they are placed in an environment where no stimulation is offered.

It could be said that under-stimulation is literally the hobgoblin of little minds. An under-stimulated brain actually begins to atrophy, shrink, and deteriorate.

In fact, chronic under-stimulation can lead to halluc-inations, delusions and confusion. The brain needs a certain amount of stimulation to function properly, and it needs interaction with the environment. Lacking this, it will manufacture its own beliefs and behaviors.

Some older people talk to themselves not because they are mentally ill, but merely because talking is their only source of stimulation. Rocking, wandering, ritualistic behavior and masturbation also provide sensory stimulation.

Regardless of a person's age, exposing him or her to new experiences and novel environments can actually cause neurons to grow new connections. Stimulation helps the brain stay healthy. Therefore, the more active the person remains, the better her memory will function.

RECEPTORS

Information coming from the outside world is picked up by millions of specialized cells called *receptors*. Eyes, ears, mouth and skin all contain receptors.

Although we all process this information in the same

manner, most of us have a preferred mode of processing information. For example, visually oriented people would rather watch something, while people with a preference for sound would rather hear it. This preference for a specific type of information is caused by the action of *stimulus filters,* which we'll talk about in a moment.

RECEPTOR PROBLEMS

For any stimulus to be picked up by the nervous system, it must be strong enough to trigger the receptor. Scientists call this minimum intensity the *stimulus threshold.* A mosquito is often able to land on the body, puncture the skin, and leave without our awareness because its delicate touch is below the stimulus threshold of the touch receptors in the skin. We only become aware of the insect's visit because of the itching caused by the bite.

And it's here that many memory problems begin. As people age, stimulus thresholds increase. Older people lose sensitivity to touch, taste, smell and sounds. Because people cannot remember what they do not perceive, when receptors fail to transmit information, no memory is stored.

For example, aging causes the sense of touch to falter. As the skin loses some of its ability to detect stimuli, people become less aware of clothing and personal items such as jewelry.

For this reason, they may not notice when an item falls off or becomes lost. Later, they may discover that they have lost a favorite sweater or a piece of jewelry, but have no conscious recollection what happened.

Elderly eyes dim, and ears no longer hear as well as

they once did. This decrease in function is usually slow and insidious, and may not be noticed for a considerable time.

Many people will deny that they have a hearing problem even when it is apparent to others around them. As hearing begins to fail, they complain that others are not speaking clearly or loudly enough. They misunderstand and misinterpret what they hear (more information about hearing loss appears in chapter 11).

Of course, when hearing fails, auditory memory suffers—what cannot be heard cannot be remembered. For this reason, people begin to exhibit what looks like memory problems, when what is actually happening is a loss of the ability to detect or understand sound.

It's important to be aware that many older people also lose much of their ability to smell and taste. This often results in a decrease in the pleasure of eating. When eating decreases, malnutrition may occur, which can have a profound effect on memory and cognition.

Screening a resident for receptor problems is a good first step in evaluating behavior problems. Checking sight, hearing, touch, taste, and smell can often pinpoint and correct problems before they become debilitating and disruptive.

STIMULUS FILTERS

Although we encounter millions of bits of information each day, we actually remember only a small portion of them. But what we *do* remember is controlled by the mechanism of filtering.

Like any filter, this mechanism eliminates unwanted material. Stimulus filters scan all incoming information, and allow into consciousness only the most important data of the moment.

Each person inherits a unique set of stimulus filters—an array of natural talents and abilities that make it easy to remember certain types of information. This is true in part because of individual differences in the hard wiring of the brain.

Just as people differ in hair color, eye color, and height, each person's brain structure is unique. In the last few years, researchers have actually found physical differvencies in brain structure that correspond with different abilities and professions.

So, while some people excel in certain types of memor, others suffer specific deficits. These people are said to have *learning disabilities*. Like their younger counterparts, elderly people with learning disabilities may be unable to process certain types of information, and therefore cannot store it. This deficit in storage has often been mistaken for a memory problem, but it's actually a processing problem. Because learning disabilities are seldom considered in the elderly, these problems are usually chalked up as dementia. But it's not dementia —it's a faulty filter.

The process by which stimulus filters decides what is to be attended to is called the *orienting response*. Orienting is an automatic, unconscious process. It is active even when we are sleeping. It is this reflex that allows a new mother to sleep through the noise of a police siren, only to be awakened a moment later by a slight whimper from her newborn.

While having a conversation with someone in a room full of people, we automatically focus on what the other person is saying. Without effort, all other conversations are filtered out. But if someone across the room calls our name, the orienting response refocuses our attention, and we turn our heads to see who called us. This ability to engage in selective listening is called the *cocktail party phenomenon.*

FILTERING PROBLEMS

As people age, input becomes harder to filter. Background noises begin to interfere with attention and concentration. Too much stimulation is confusing and distracting. People react to this by withdrawing. This is one reason why residents in long term care facilities prefer to stay in their rooms—the outside world becomes too noisy and confusing.

Stress also causes stimulus filters to break down, and when filters break, nothing in the environment gets filtered out.

This causes stimulus *overload.* Short-term memory can't handle this much input. When this happens, the person becomes unable to focus, and therefore is unable to transfer the information into long-term memory.

The net result is that the brain stops processing new information. Later on, when the stress is over, people find they can't remember events that happened during the time of stress.

In addition, a stressed person is preoccupied with concerns about being stressed. This preoccupation not only interferes with the ability to learn new information, it can block the person's ability to recall what she already knows.

When older people feel stressed, they instinctively try to get away from noise and distraction they can no longer filter. This is where that phrase "getting away from it all" came from. Some of the isolating behavior residents engage in is actually an attempt at reducing stress.

In these cases, providing the person with quieter surroundings, less stimulation, and an uninterrupted flow of information will improve both the ability to store and to recall information

As mentioned earlier, it's common for new residents in a care facility to experience a great deal of stress. Everything around them is new and different. This frequently results in temporary confusion and memory loss. As the person becomes familiar with the facility, these problems go away. (For more on confusion, see chapter 5.)

SHORT TERM MEMORY

Once a piece of information has been selected by the orienting response, and passed through the stimulus filter for processing, it enters *short term memory*. Short term memory holds only a small amount of information —enough for about one phone number—and holds it for a very short period of time—about twenty or thirty seconds.

You've probably had the experience of looking up a number in a phone book, walking over to the phone, dialing part of the number, and suddenly realizing that you have forgotten the rest of it. What do you do? You look the number up again, and this time say the number over and over to yourself until you reach the phone. If you're successful in dialing the number, you finish your conversation, and hang up. But if you have to call again in a few minutes, you find you have again forgotten the number. These are the limitations of short term storage.

Contrary to popular belief, elderly people seldom lose their short-term memory. Even people suffering from advanced dementia can often carry on a sensible conversation.

Because their short-term memory and their language function is intact, they appear normal. However, a moment after a conversation has ended, they have absolutely no memory of it. Conversations go like this:

> I introduce myself to Mrs. Irwin, saying, "Hi, Mrs. Irwin. My name is Dr. Cone."
> "Hi, Dr. Cone," she replied, "That's an easy name to remember, isn't it?"
> "Sure is," I said, "Can you tell me how long you've been here?"
> "A few days," she told me. (She had actually been here for six months).
> "Do you know my name?" I asked.
> "I don't believe you told me your name."

Short term memory is still working. But what *is* lost is *the ability to transfer the information* from short-term to long-term memory. People can hold onto an idea long enough to respond to it, but a fleeting moment later, it is whisked away and gone forever.

LONG TERM MEMORY

The final stage in the memory process is the retrieval the stored information. Most of the time, the inability to remember something is caused by a failure in the storage process just described. The most common cause of not remembering is the simple failure of information being transferred from short-term to long-term memory.

One way to help the memory impaired to store information in long term memory is to repeat it many times in many places, and to review it frequently.

Repetition sends a message to the memory that the information is important and should be stored. Repeating information many times in many circumstances causes an increase in *cue density*, and increases the person's ability to store and recall new information. Even in people with noticeable memory problems, repetition and spaced- practice often result in learning.

Another way to increase learning is through the use of pictures. Have the resident draw a picture that corresponds with the information they wish to learn. If they are unable to draw, do it for them. For example, when I want a person to remember my name, I tell them, " My name is Dr. Cone, like ice cream cone," and I have them draw picture of an ice cream cone.

RETRIEVAL PROBLEMS

As people get older, retrieval of information takes longer. Even in people with normal memory, search and retrieval slows down with age. Word finding also becomes more difficult. Studies show that the first category of words that become inaccessible are proper names. This is followed by nouns, adjectives, and then verbs.

When a person tells you they cannot remember something, ask the question in a different way. This causes other pathways to be activated, and increases the chance of recall. If this doesn't work, ask the question again later—what is unavailable at one moment can be recalled without effort a few moments later.

REMOTE MEMORY

Family members of elderly people often remark about the person's remarkable ability to remember events from years ago, but not from last week

Remote memory is the storehouse for the events of childhood and youth. Unlike other types of memory, this type is durable and long lasting. Even in the intermediate stages of dementia, remote memory usually stays intact.

People with memory problems remember remote events better than recent one's for several reasons. First, as just stated, remote memory is the last type of memory to be affected by dementia.

Second, people often tell the same stories over and over, which keeps the memory fresh in their minds.

Third, it's impossible to tell whether these memories are accurate. Because they happened so long ago, there is usually no way to verify them. Even if the stories are recounted with conviction, they may have little resemblance to what actually happened.

And finally, many older people don't remember recent events well because their life is dull, repetitive, and uninteresting. You see, when nothing memorable happens, nothing is remembered.

Chapter five

CONFUSION

Have you ever awakened in a hotel room in the middle of the night and had no idea where you were? Perhaps you didn't remember until you'd groped for your glasses and turned on a light.

Now imagine that you're in a hospital. You have bilateral cataracts, are hard of hearing, and took a sleeping pill a few hours ago. You're awakened by the presence of a shadowy figure. Alarmed and still drowsy from the medication, you strike out at the intruder.

After she leaves, you try to get up to urinate, but what are those bars on the bed? You climb over them and tumble to the floor. As you lie there, you lose control of your bladder. The shadowy figure returns, straps you back in bed, and sticks a tube into your bladder. Then she goes to the nurses' station where she writes in your chart, "Confused, combative, and incontinent."

According to Gayle Anderson, the expert in geriatric assessment who wrote the words above, about half of the people entering a care facility will go through a period of disorientation. But this is only one of many causes of confusion.

Behavioral Objectives

At the end of this section readers will be able to:

Define differences between disorientation, confusion and delirium

Help people with disorientation

List the causes of confusion

Discuss medical causes of confusion

Causes of confusion

Infections:

> acute meningitis
> viral
> chronic meningitis
> tuberculosis
> fungal
> neurosyphilis
> subdural empyema
> brain abscess
> pneumonia
> pyelonephritis
> cholecystitis
> diverticulitis
> endocarditis

Hypo or Hyperthermia

Hypoxia:
(decreased cerebral oxygen)

> acute myocardial infarction
> congestive heart failure
> arrhythmia
> vascular occlusion
> pulmonary embolism
> hypotension
> transient ischemia (TIA)
> ventilatory failure
> chronic lung disease

Anemic hypoxia:

> iron deficiency anemia
> pernicious anemia
> folic acid deficiency
> gradual blood loss

Brain Disorders

> head trauma
> subdural hematoma
> concussion/contusion
> epidural hematoma
> intracerebral hemorrhage
> Normal-pressure
> hydrocephalus

Many elderly people become bewildered. The words we use for this condition are confusion, delirium, and disorientation. Although all three words describe a confused individual, they mean different things, and the distinctions are often important to treatment.

DISORIENTATION

Disorientation means the lack of awareness of time, place, and person. It is the specific loss of ability to know where you are, what time it is, what day, month, season, or year it is. Disorientation can be caused by dementia, confusion, or delirium, but it can also be a function of the person's environment and lifestyle. For example Some hospital wards have no windows, which makes it impossible to tell whether it is day or night. Some facilities have few clocks, calendars, of any other external cues to orient the person.

In addition it must be kept in mind that many elderly people have lost their sense of time because every day is exactly the same. While structure is important, complete lack of change makes the days pass by uneventfully. This not only leads to disorientation, but impairs memory. Children of elderly parents often comment that their parents remember things that happened years ago, but not what happened last week. This is caused in part by the fact that nothing happened last week!

INTERVENTIONS FOR DISORIENTATION

1. Make sure the environment has cues for orientation.

The environment should contain clocks. Calendars, signs stating the day, month and year. There should also be signs stating the name and location of the facility.

2. Structure each day differently, so that the

48

week contains different daily activities.

Elderly people do not get weekends off. They do not have regularly scheduled vacations. Unless their is a clear way for them to tell one day from another, they will lose orientation to time.

DELIRIUM

Delirium, also called *acute confusional state* (ACS) is most often caused by acute illness, or drug toxicity and always involves periods of diminished conscious-ness. It may also be caused by fever, organ failure which leads to toxicity, or any acute infection.

Delirium is a sign of danger, and if not treated, often is a warning sign of death. The delirious state is usually transient and fluctuates in intensity. In the majority of cases, the person recovers within four weeks. However, in elderly patients, delirium lasting up to 6 months is not uncommon, especially when arising because of chronic liver disease, a carcinoma, or subacute bacterial endo-carditis.

CONFUSION

Confusion is a group of behaviors that include dis-tractability, an impaired attention span, loss of memory for recent events and later for remote events, impaired judgement, inability to comprehend the environment, and the inability to understand or follow instructions. Unlike delirium, confusion does not always include loss of alertness, and is not always cased by a medical condition.

None of these terms include all behavior—few people become confused about everything, are constantly delirious, or remain totally disoriented. Instead, these conditions are usually intermittent and patchy in occur-rence.

Causes of reversible confusion

Metabolic Imbalances:

Renal failure
Dehydration
Hyponatremia (low salt)
Hypernatremia (high salt)
Blood volume depletion
Acid-base imbalance
Hypoglycemia
Hyperglycemia
Liver failure
Hypothyroidism
Hyperthyroidism
Hypercalcemia
Hypopituitarism
Cushing's Syndrome

Physical:

Fractures
Recent surgery
Fecal Impaction
Urinary retention

Environmental:

Relocation
A sudden change in environment
Sleep Deprivation
Sensory Deprivation
Sudden change in temperature
Sudden Change in food habits
Adding or stopping a medication
Catastrophic loss (such as death of spouse)
Sudden change in daily activity schedule

Drugs that cause delerium

Antiparkinsonian Drugs

Amantadine
(Symmetrel)

Carbidopa/levodopa
(Sinemet)

Levodopa(Larodopa)

CNS Depressants

Meperidine
(Demerol)

Codeine

Morphine
Hydromorphone
(Dilaudid)

Tricyclic antidepressants

Amitriptyline
(Elavil)

Doxepin

Imipramine
(Tofranil)

Nortriptyline
(Pamelor)

This is important, because if the assumption is made that the symptoms are the result of old age or senility, and that they are irreversible, care givers may overlook a potentially dangerous medical condition, or unnecessarily restrict a person's rights.

Irreversible confusional states *are* found in about 50% of the institutionalized elderly and in a large number who are cared for by families. These types of confusion are caused by brain damage, are progressive, and are collectively known as *dementias* (More information on dementia appears in chapter 6). Alzheimer's disease or multi-infarct dementia account for 80% of the dementias of old age. However, much of what may look like dementia can, in many cases, be reversed.

REVERSIBLE CONFUSION

One of the diagnostic distinctions between permanent and reversible confusion is that the latter type usually has a *rapid onset.* There is often a sudden loss of cognition, orientation and memory for recent events. During this time, the person may have visual hallucinations and the inability to organize thoughts or actions. Even so, the person's orientation and social protocols may be unimpaired.

The person suffering this type of cognitive impairment has trouble following directions or focusing on anything for any meaningful length of time. Later, when the person is no longer confused, he may be able to remember his own thoughts and actions as if he saw them in a movie.

There are many causes of confusion, most of which are caused by a major change in the person's physical or emotional state. Confusion often happens after surgery, an accident, an illness, or because of an acute metabolic imbalance.

But even though confusion is usually caused by a medical condition, the confused behavior may actually be the first sign of the problem. In the margins of these pages is a partial list of conditions which can cause confusion.

The treatment for rapid onset confusional states should begin immediately. This means obtaining an accurate assessment, screening, diagnoses, and a close observation of the person's behavior.

INTERVENTIONS FOR CONFUSION

1. Do a complete physical examination, along with a basic laboratory screening.

Check the person's vital signs. The assessments should also include testing for mental impairment, and a comparison of historical information to recent changes in the person's behavior. Ask about the person's personal history and life-style. Assess his ability to follow directions and maintain attention to the events around him.

2. If there is no evidence of disease of metabolic imbalance, consider recent life events which could have caused undue stress.

Look at factors like recent losses, change in visits, and changes in the environment.

3. Use frequent statements of orientation

These statement help the person restore his contact with reality while the physical and social stressors are being assessed and treated. Here is an example of an effective intervention:

Drugs that cause delirium

Anticholinergics

Atropine
Benzotropine (Cogentin)

Scopalamine
(Methyexyphenidyl
trihexane)

Benzodiazapines

Taken alone:

Diazepam (Valium)

Temazepam (Restoril)

Triazolam (Halcion)

Taken alone or in
combination with
Tagamet:

Alprazolam (Xanax)

Clorazepate (Gen-Xene)

Tranxene

Flurazepam (Dalmane)

Prarepam (Centrax)

Mrs. Harris was being admitted to the hospital because of wandering, incontinence, disorientation to time and place, and several chronic medical conditions. She was frightened and disoriented. During the admission process she continued to cry out, "Help me, I can't get out of here, help me, I'm lost!"

The nurse was able to calm her through touch and repeating the statements, "Mrs. Harris, I am Mrs. Posner. Look at my name tag. See it has my name and the name of this hospital on it. I'm your nurse. You are in Alameda Hospital. I will be caring for you. This is your room, here is your bed, and this is where we are going to put your belongings. You are perfectly safe."

This repeated intervention eventually oriented the person to her new surroundings.

The treatment for reversible confusion always consists of *treating the cause*. For example, the treatment for confusion from dehydration is to relieve the dehydration while maintaining the safety of the person. The treatment for pernicious anemia is to begin immediate vitamin B_{12} replacement.

Confusion which comes from relocation, sudden environmental changes, sensory overload, and other environmental stressors, improves only when the stress in the environment is identified and reduced. If these things are not addressed, any behavioral intervention will be ineffective.

Chapter six

DEMENTIA

The word *dementia* means literally to lose ones's mind. Dementia is a syndrome of brain dysfunction characterized by multiple deficits in cognitive abilities without loss of alertness (a loss of alertness occurs in *delirium*).

In 1900 there were 3 million people over 65 in the United States. At the time of this writing, there are about 35 million, and this number is expected to double by the year 2050. It is estimated that one percent of people between the ages of 65 and 74 years old, seven percent of those from 75 to 84 years old, and twenty-five percent of those over 85 suffer from severe dementia. Currently about 2 million people in the U.S. suffer from advanced dementia, while another 5 million suffer mild-to-moderate symptoms.

Dementia is caused by *brain damage*. The parts of the brain that are most affected are the association areas of the brain, which integrate sensory information, thought, memory, and purposeful behavior.

When extensive damage to these regions occurs, the

Behavioral Objectives

At the end of this sections readers will be able to:

Describe the general progression from the early through the late stage of Alzheimer=s

Assess the extent of memory and cognitive loss in a person

Communicate effectively with a person suffering from dementia

List the behavioral complications of dementia

person may begin to engage in bizarre behaviors that have no external link to the environment. They may also become verbally and physically agitated and abusive.

Dementia always includes the loss of memory *and* cognition. It also causes the loss of the ability to make sound judgements, and to maintain an ongoing sense of being. Very often, the ability to comprehend and express ideas is also impaired. And there are problems with social interaction, daily living skills, and thinking.,

There are over 60 known disorders that cause dementia, but Alzheimer's disease, which is also often referred to as D*ementia of the Alzheimer's type* (DAT), accounts for over half of all dementias. Vascular disease, called *multi-infarct dementia* or *vascular dementia* accounts for another twenty percent.

In addition, some people suffer from potentially reversible dementias caused by brain tumors, infections, toxins, nutritional deficiencies, over-medication, metabolic problems, and other neurological disorders.

It is also important to distinguish the existence of a mental disorder from the symptoms of dementia, because mental disorders often mimic the symptoms of dementia, but are treatable. In addition, when a person is suffering from dementia, the existence of a mental disorder may worsen the symptoms.

For a person suffering from dementia, the move from home to a care giving facility is very difficult. Already confused, they lose of most of what has become familiar. They lose their homes, friends, lifestyles, familiar objects, and much of their independence.

This sense of multiple loss, when combined with the cognitive and memory problems caused by dementia, usually causes new residents to have extreme difficulty adjusting to their new environment—in short, they don't know where they are or where there personal belongings have gone, and they get scared.

THE STAGES OF DEMENTIA

Early Stage

Have you ever walked into a room and realized you had no idea why you were there? Demented people experience this every day.

In the early stages of dementia, the loss of ability to think and remember becomes intermittent and patchy— the afflicted person may forget who you are on Monday, but have no trouble recognizing you a day later.

A person in the early stage of Alzheimer's disease may begin to show a loss of interest in his environment and in his personal affairs. Word finding becomes difficult, usually beginning with the inability to remember names, and then nouns. He may have difficulty in attending to important social events, such as holidays or birthday parties. Social graces, politeness, and social protocols begin to break down. For example, one of my patients went home in the middle of his birthday party, because he did not remember why he was there, and decided it was time to take a nap.

People in this stage suffer uncertainty and confusion in initiating actions. A thought occurs to the person to do something, but a moment after they begin, they have forgotten what they intended to do. They may pick up an object with clear intent, and find themselves wandering around with it, not remembering what they meant to do.

At this stage of the illness, people may be able to live at home with supportive care. But even though they appear to be thinking clearly, they will usually need assistance in paying bills and managing money. Frequent assistance is especially important if the person lives alone.

Proper health care, vitamin E, Vitamin B_{12} and non-steroidal anti-inflammatory drugs, and anticholinesterase inhibiting drugs—along with the reduction of environmental change and stress—can reduce symptoms, slow the disease process and prolong independence at this stage.

Although a person in this stage of the disease may still be able to drive, he may become easily lost, and forget his way home. Neighbors and friends can assist by being aware of any change in living habits which warrant increased vigilance. Relocation, change in residence, or illness will often be the point at which the patient slips into the next stage.

Intermediate Stage

As dementia progresses there is a loss of what health care providers call *activities of daily living* (ADL). Health care and personal hygiene are neglected. The person shows diminished ability to care for personal needs or affairs. There is also a loss of ability to comprehend, remember, or follow simple directions. As motor programs begin to break down, the person may engage in meaningless behavior.

There are obvious memory problems, in recall, recognition, and retention. As memory loss continues, most of the simple tasks of life—like bathing, brushing teeth, or getting dressed—become confusing and incomprehensible, and require aid from others. Even something as simple as putting on a shirt may become overwhelming.

Biological clocks begin to falter, and time disorient-ation occurs to the degree that the person may not be able to tell if it is day or night—the victim wakes at midnight and asks for lunch. Appointments are forgotten and personal possessions are lost or sometimes hoarded and hidden.

Because there are severe deficits in the ability to think and remember, business affairs must be turned over to a conservator or family member with power of attorney. At this point, families may still be able to care for the person, if there is support for its members. If a support network is not in place, most families find the care giving over-whelming, and a higher level of care is required.

Later Stage

As the disease progresses screaming, wandering aimlessly, and combative behaviors appear. The person in the later stage of Alzheimer's disease is no longer able to find his way from one point to another. He often is disoriented as to time and place. His ability to recognize people becomes impaired, and he may mistake a care giver for a family member. Fine motor skills, such as the ability to write and manipulate objects, are lost. The person now need help with eating, getting dressed, and toileting.

Speech becomes garbled and incoherent and non-verbal communication must often be used. A compulsive need to touch everything, to hoard everything, and to examine all objects with the mouth begins to emerge.

There is sometimes a complete loss of emotion. Dietary habits change, ranging from anorexia to binge eating. The person may exhibit inappropriate sexual behavior. Even with all of these problems, a person in this phase may still be able to engage in and enjoy physical activities such as walking and group activities, and will still enjoy music.

By this time, behavior literally falls to pieces. Motor programs are shattered into fragments. The person may suddenly get up, stop, look around, touch the wall, and sit down again without having the slightest idea what they are doing.

By this time the person requires 24-hour care. Placement in a care facility may become necessary. When this is done, the lack of familiar surroundings and faces often results in a total loss of orientation. Personal hygiene is done entirely by a care giver. Sleep becomes severely impaired, and agitation and confusion often occur upon awakening, and before bedtime.

Terminal Stage

In the end stage of this cruel siege, the individual may lose the ability to walk or stand up, and the ability to communicate in any meaningful way. The terminal stage requires total nursing care. The patient is dependent on support for all physiologic processes. He is non-responsive and cannot not recognize family members or familiar objects. Further deterioration is usually halted by death from an infection, renal failure, or pneumonia.

ASSISTING FAMILIES

Losing a loved one to this disease is a painful and devastating process. Family members undergo prolonged anticipatory grief and require frequent support from the staff and from each other. Some family members may not be able to tolerate seeing the mindless, ravaged body of a person who no longer recognizes them. Occasionally, to protect themselves from the pain, they stop visiting the patient. Supporting the family members is vitally important in preventing abandonment at this time.

INTERVENTIONS FOR WORKING WITH DEMENTIA PATIENTS

Behavioral complications of dementia include depression, wandering, endless pacing, aggression, agitation hallucinations, paranoia, disturbed sleep, inappropriate verbalizations, rummaging, pica (eating non-edible items), hyper-sexuality, self-abuse, and repetitive questioning. Many of these problems are discussed later in this book.

Communicating with a person who is suffering from dementia requires skill and patience. Here are some suggestions:

1. Never approach a person from behind.

You will startle and upset them.

2. Stand directly in front of the person when you are speaking to them.

Touch their arm or shoulder gently to focus their attention.

3. Always treat the person with dignity and respect.

4. People with dementia are very sensitive to nonverbal communication.

Even when they have lost the ability to understand what you are saying, they will react to your delivery. Your tone of voice and facial expression are more important than your words.

5. Speak slowly and simply, but remember

that the demented person is an adult.

Although you may have to speak slowly and simply, avoid talking to them as if they were children.

6. Assess the person's ability to comprehend verbal commands.

Research shows that as dementia progresses, people lose the ability to comprehend complex verbal commands. However, even those with relatively advanced dementia maintain their ability to comprehend single stage commands. You can do a quick assessment of the person's comprehension ability by asking them several one-, two-, and three-step commands. An example of this is:

One-step: Close your eyes.

Pick up the brush.

Two-step: Pick up the brush and give it to me.

Pick up the paper, and put it in the book.

Three-step: Take this piece of paper, fold it in half, and place it inside the drawer.

Pick up the book, put the paper in it, and hand it to me.

If the person can comprehend and respond to three step commands, use them. Using one step commands with these people will not maintain their attention. For those with impaired comprehension, use one-step commands and yes or no questions.

7. Don't expect a quick response.

People with impaired thinking skills take longer to comprehend what was said to them. Give the person time to comprehend and respond to what you've said.

8. Demented people often have difficulty in word finding.

They may say one word but mean another, and you may have to guess at the correct meaning. Pay attention to the voice and gestures for clues. Provide the proper word, and ask them if this is what they meant.

9. Use gestures and visual clues to clarify what you mean.

10. If you must repeat something, use the same words.

11. Discuss only concrete actions and objects, not abstract concepts.

12. Don't force a person to engage in conversation.

If the person has difficulty speaking or comprehending what is said, conversation will make them feel inadequate. They will react to this by becoming agitated.

13. Avoid asking questions whenever possible.

Answering a question requires searching one's memory, forming a thought and translating the thought into speech, which is difficult for a person with a malfunctioning brain. Not knowing the answers embarrasses and upsets people. Because of this, when they cannot answer a question, they often become agitated and snap something like, "Stop asking so many stupid questions!"

It's important to be aware that people suffering from dementia cannot store memory. This means that no matter how many times you tell them something, they will forget it a moment later. This is frustrating for care givers because although they may get to know residents quite well, and spend months helping them, the residents have absolutely no memory of them or what they have done.

14. Use Musical Cues

Since even advanced dementia patients retain memory of music, specific pieces of music can be used to announce activities such as mealtime and bedtime, or to identify bathrooms and eating areas.

Chapter seven

DEPRESSION

In healthy adults, depression beginning late in life is uncommon. In fact, less than one percent of the healthy elderly suffer from depression. Despite the occasional inconveniences that accompany aging most older adults actually experience an increase in life satisfaction.

On the other hand, depression is prevalent in many older people who are medically ill, and the greater the severity of the illness, the more likely it is that a person will develop depression. For this reason, depression in the elderly is seen to a great extent among disabled, hospitalized, and long-term care patients.

Depressive symptoms are found in 40-50 percent of nursing home and geropsychiatric hospital residents, and in a recent study of several nursing homes, major depression was found in twenty-five percent of the cognitively intact residents and ten percent of cognitively impaired residents.

It is vitally important that all elderly people be screened for depression, because depression in cognitively intact individuals can mimic the signs of

Behavioral Objectives

At the end of this section readers will be able to

Describe the extend of depression in the elderly

List the symptoms of depression

Discriminate between grief, sadness, and depression

Discuss the medical causes of depression

dementia, while depression in people with cognitive problems can make their problems worse.

Research suggests that depression has a genetic component, that is, depression runs in families. But unlike depression in early life, genetic factors seem to be less important in depression that starts late in life.

Despite the high prevalence of depression, elderly people seldom admit to being depressed. Instead, they often have multiple physical complaints. These symptoms include weight loss, agitation, anxiety and panic attacks, irritability, obsessive concern with bodily functions, constipation, a bad taste in the mouth, lack of interest in sex, frequent headaches, chronic aches and pains, and insomnia.

There is evidence that these multiple somatic complaints may be cause in part by the older person's difficulty in putting their feelings into words. The two halves of the brain communicate though a bundle of nerve fibers called the *corpus callosum*. It is thought that during the aging process, cell loss occurs in these fibers, impeding the transmission of emotions generated in the right hemisphere into the left hemisphere language centers.

The condition of being unable to express emotions is called *alexithymia* (which means literally 'no word for feelings') and has been associated with dementia as well as depression.

In the 1800's, German psychiatrist Caupp coined the phrase *arteriosclerotic depression*. Caupp observed that many elderly depressed people also showed hardening of the arteries. Felix Post also suggested that vascular disease in the brain was a significant factor in the development of depression in late life .

With the advent of computer tomography (CT) and

magnetic resonance imaging (MRI), it has become possible to evaluate subtle vascular changes in the brain of elderly patients with depression. Vascular changes are seen as hyper-intense signals both in the white matter and gray matter.

In 1988, Krishnan found that over seventy percent of patients with late-onset depression (over age 50), had hyper intense signals on the MRI images. The main locations of the gray matter changes were in the basal ganglia, in the caudate and putamen, the cingulate gyrus, and in the frontal lobes of the brain.

Depression, Grief, and Sadness

In an elderly person it's important to distinguish depression from *grief* and *sadness*. Sadness is most often a transitory state, and very often is the result of revisiting a painful memory. Temporary bouts of sadness are common on older people, as most of them have had many losses, and from time to time they will revisit these memories. In these times, refocusing a person on more pleasant thoughts can often ameliorate the feelings of dejection.

But while sadness may be a fleeting feeling, grief is a process that may last for months or years. Grief is the process of mourning a significant loss. Most elderly people, especially those in long term care facilities, have undergone several significant losses, such as the loss of spouse, loss of their home, loss of friends, and most importantly, the loss of their independence. These losses are monumental and must be grieved.

Grief has specific stages, (discussed later in this chapter) one of which is depression. But unlike depression, which may not have a recognizable cause, grief is always the result of a catastrophic loss.

Depressive symptoms

Thought

Negative self-evaluations
Negative expectations
Negative interpretation of events
Memory loss
Confusion
Impaired attention span
A focus on past mistakes
All or nothing thinking
Unwanted thoughts
Poverty of thought
Hopelessness
Helplessness
The wish to be dead
Suicidal thoughts
The conviction of being a burden

Emotion

Ambivalence
No sense of humor
Feeling inadequate
Chronic apathy
Sadness
Guilt
Powerlessness
Emotions are dulled
No motivation

Symbols

Destructive fantasies
Nightmares
Bothersome images
Punishment from God

Depressive symptoms

Behavior

A change in activity level
Aggression
Destructive acts
Crying spells
Suicide attempts
Slowed speech
Substance abuse
Impulsiveness
Violation of personal values
Agitation
Perfectionism

Relationships

A victim stance
Extreme dependency
High reactivity
Social isolation
Avoidance
Approval seeking
Martyrdom
Passive-aggressive behavior
Boundary problems
Hypercritical
Poor communication skills

Physical

Multiple physical complaints
Sleep problems
Appetite changes
Weight changes
Change in sex-drive

Losses should not be minimized, that is, care givers should never tell a person, "Cheer up, it's not so bad." This is often said in an effort to comfort a person, but it actually discounts and trivializes the losses. It is also not useful to tell a grieving person, "I understand how you must feel." Unless you have actually suffered a similar loss, you don't know how they feel.

You can never measure the extent of another person's attachment or loss, and no loss is trivial.

> Mrs. Peterson was brought to the hospital because she was losing weight, was isolating, and was suffering frequent bouts of crying. She had told others that she wanted to die. It was discovered at the intake interview that she had recently lost her parakeet—her closest companion for the last ten years. No one had recognized the enormity of her loss. In fact, the board-and-care administrator had told us, "I wish she would quit crying about that stupid bird." When this loss was validated and acknowledged, she was allowed to work it through, and eventually recovered.

Depression is also one of the most common under-diagnosed cause of memory problems. Depression has a profound effect on the ability to think, reason, and re-member. In fact, the symptoms of depression can be so severe that it's often difficult to tell whether a person is suffering from depression or dementia. Because of this, several diagnostic tests have been developed to ferret out the differences between these two memory destroying disorders.

Depressed people become focused on internal events. These may be memories about tragic losses, or about real and imagined transgressions. As just mentioned, the focus is often on physical symptoms such as body aches and pains. This internal preoccupation prevents the person from attending to the outside world.

Depression actually slows down the level of brain activity in the afflicted person, so that memory and thought processing are impaired. People suffering from depression often are said to exhibit *poverty of thought,* which is the inability to process thought at all.

Depression is accompanied by feelings of helplessness and hopelessness. This leads the sufferer to ignore any input from the outside world—they just don't care about anything.

Depression has also been linked to decreased levels of chemicals in the brain, called *neurotransmitters.* The neurotransmitters involved in depression include *serotonin, melatonin, dopamine, adrenaline,* and *noradrenaline,* substances which also play an important role in memory. It is believed that antidepressant drugs work by raising the levels of these chemicals.

DRUGS THAT CAUSE DEPRESSION

Although depression is most often caused by loss, isolation, or a biochemical imbalance in the brain, it can also be caused by nutritional deficiencies or excesses, prescription, over-the-counter, and illegal drugs, alcohol, caffeine and nicotine, hypoglycemia, and hormonal imbalances. In fact, research suggests that almost any chronic biochemical imbalance can cause depression.

Many medications, used alone or in combinations, may cause depressions. Often, reducing the dosages, elimination of use, or chaining certain combinations will correct the problem. Here are a few of the most common culprits.

Drugs that cause Depression

Digitalis

Clonidine

Levodopa

Antipsychotics

Propranolol

Reserpine

Cimetidine

Methyldopate

Barbiturates

Benzodiazepines

Steroids

Alcohol

Gaunethidine

Anti-emetics

Sedatives

Tranquilizers

Hypertension Medications

Bicarbonate

Antiemetics

Antiemetic drugs are used to prevent nausea. But if they are used in large doses or over a period of time, they may cause depression. If this is the cause, discontinuing the drug or using a smaller dose usually reverses the symptoms in two weeks.

Sedatives

Unfortunately, sedative drugs are often used by elderly people to promote sleep and reduce anxiety. Instead they often lead to addiction, abuse and an increased risk of depression and suicide. Because of this problem, some states now use computer tracking to see if the person is obtaining these medications from more than one doctor.

Corticosteroids

Steroid drugs, used as anti-inflammatories, often cause depression, which usually occurs late rather than early in their use.

Antihypertensives

Blood pressure medications can also cause depression and subsequent behavioral problems. Even though this is common knowledge, many doctors are unaware of how often people suffer from drug-induced depression, and fail to connect depressive symptoms with the medication.

Harvard researcher Dr. Jerry Avorn and his colleagues looked at how often antidepressants were prescribed to people taking beta-blockers such as *Inderal*, *Lopressor*, and *Corgard*. Examining the medical records of 143,253 residents, they found that 23 percent (almost one out of four) of those taking beta-blockers were also taking anti-depressants.

This study revealed that doctors often give patients additional prescriptions to overcome side effects of another medication without realizing that the problems could actually be solved by eliminating the first medication.

Bicarbonate

Ingestion of large amounts of bicarbonate may lead to depressive symptoms. In addition, the vomiting of gastric acid and respiratory acidosis cause a rise in the plasma bicarbonate level. Many patients who have anxiety or hysteric vomiting attacks take over the counter bicarbonate as a relief, which eventually causes depression. Also, antacids used in the treatment of ulcers may alter the person's electrolyte balance and cause depression.

NUTRIENTS AND DEPRESSION

Calcium

Excessive milk drinking, steroid hormone therapy, and hypothyroidism can all contribute to a condition called *hypercalcemia*, which may lead to depression.

Magnesium

The most common group to experience a magnesium deficit are chronic alcoholics. Depression is commonly linked to both alcoholism and alcohol withdrawal, and magnesium sulfate can often reverse the depression.

Potassium

Although the exact mechanism is not known, excess potassium has bee associated with depression. This is often seen in uremic patients. A deficiency of potassium is also associated with depression and is most commonly seen in patients with frequent vomiting or prolonged diarrhea and people receiving diuretics or steroids.

Sodium

Elderly people with heart problems, particularly those in cardiac failure, sometimes eliminate sodium from their diets. Because of this they may develop depression. In these cases the addition of a minimal amount of sodium corrects the problem.

Vitamin C

In a few cases, chronic vitamin C deficiency has been shown to cause both *hypochondriasis* (a preoccupation with bodily symptoms) and depression. In addition, vitamin C has been shown to interact with many central nervous system receptors.

B_{12} and Folic Acid

Folic acid and B_{12} levels have been found to be low in a large proportion of residents suffering from various emotional problems, especially depression. But although B_{12} deficiency is common in depression, measuring levels of B_{12} in the blood is not always useful. B_{12} deficiency may not become apparent until long after serum levels have been greatly reduced, and depression has begun.

In studies of elderly people with depression, as many as 30 percent were shown to be deficient in folic acid. In another study, 67 percent of the residents admitted to a geropsychiatric hospital were deficient. As well as depression, folic acid deficiency can also cause chronic forgetfulness, insomnia, apathy, and dementia-like symptoms.

Niacin and Biotin

Both niacin (vitamin B_3) deficiency and biotin deficiency can exacerbate depression and memory problems, as well as cause emotional instability, while pantothenic acid (vitamin B_5) deficiency can cause restlessness, irritability, and depression.

Thiamin

Thiamin (vitamin B_1) deficiency is very common among alcoholics, and can lead to a condition called Korsakoff's psychosis, which causes profound memory loss, as well as depression, apathy, anxiety and irritability. B_1 deficiency in the brain results in a condition called *metabolic acidosis*, which upsets the neurotransmitter balance.

In addition to medication problems, depression can sometimes be caused by allergies to environmental toxins. For example, solvents like those used in paints, furniture making, and boat building have been reported to cause depression, confusion, and memory loss in many people.

Although rare, another potential cause is chronic exposure to heavy metals. Because elderly people may have an impaired ability to eliminate toxins from the body, these factors should be ruled out before further intervention.

Depression is often one of the first signs of thyroid disease. Even subtle decreases in thyroid hormone can induce depression, and in the elderly depression may be the only sign of thyroid dysfunction. For this reason, depressed residents should be routinely screened for thyroid problems, particularly if they complain of depression and fatigue.

Physical conditions that can cause depression

Alzheimer's Disease

Multiple Sclerosis

Tertiary Syphilis

Adrenal Cortex Dysfunction

Hyperinsulinism

Hypoparthyroidism

Corticosteroids

Electrolyte Disorders

Excess Calcium

Potassium imbalance

Low sodium

Tumors

Stroke

Like the thyroid gland, dysfunction of the adrenal gland has been associated with depression, so adrenal function should also be checked.

Temporal lobe tumors are particularly inclined to cause depression, and are frequently masked by the psychological symptoms of headache and paresthesias.

POST-STROKE DEPRESSION

Although they are usually easy to diagnose, strokes —with or without physical impairment or disability— often cause depression. Strokes may be major or minor, and minor ones may produce as severe a depression as a major stroke.

The most effective treatment for post stroke depression is antidepressant drug therapy.

PSYCHOTIC DEPRESSION

The term *psychotic depression* was quite common prior to the 1940's. In fact, during that time as many as two-thirds of hospitalized depressed patients were diagnosed as psychotically depressed. Today the term has fallen out of favor, and less than ten percent of depressed patients are considered psychotic.

Nevertheless, psychotic depression happens frequently in the elderly. This type of depression often mimics dementia, and can include hallucinations, delusions, and other bizarre symptoms. It's important to remember that depression alone can cause psychotic symptoms. When a person becomes delusional or begins to hallucinate, depression could be the cause.

About two thirds of psychotically depressed people have delusions but no hallucinations, and about one quarter have hallucinations without delusions. Patients often claim that their insides are rotting.

The most common delusion seen in psychotically depressed people is the *delusion of persecution*—the belief that other people are wishing the person harm. Often, the person feels that they deserve to be punished. Some say that they are evil and that God is punishing them. Elderly patients who express intense feelings of guilt and remorse should always be screened for psychotic symptoms.

Other contributing factors to depression can be physical problems such as hearing loss, vision problems, foot problems, and even dental problems.

> I was once called for a consultation for a patient who had been isolating, refusing to leave her room, and refusing to participate in groups or mealtime. Although this woman had a history of depression, during the interview she told me, "I'm not leaving this room until I get my new dentures. I look so ugly without my teeth." In this case, a dental consultation cured the problem.

BEHAVIORAL INTERVENTIONS FOR DEPRESSION

1. Take a loss history and assess for unresolved grief.

2. Get a baseline measure of depression.

Using a depression scale such as the Geriatric Depression scale or the Hamilton Depression Scale. Using these scales is an easy and effective way to measure the patient's progress

3. Help the person recognize faulty thought processes.

Encourage the person to talk about his negative

thoughts, doubts, and fears. Make a list of these thoughts, and then ask the person to furnish evidence that the thoughts are true. Point out to him that most of is negative thoughts are not based on any objective evidence.

4. Teach constructive thought processes.

Teach them problem solving and coping skills. Help them define problems clearly, and set goals to solve them constructively.

5. Help the person recognize their strengths and abilities.

Help the person construct a list of her positive qualities. If she cannot do this, tell her what you find likeable about her.

6. Construct a *hedonic scale*.

This is a list of all the activities the resident used to enjoy. Once the list is made, have them rate how much they think they would enjoy the activity now on a scale of one to ten.

Once they have done this, have them engage in one of the activities. When they are finished, have them rate how much they actually enjoyed the activity. Depressed people under-rate their expected enjoyment. When they realize that they can actually enjoy the things they once did, they become more willing to do them again.

7. Help them begin a life review

Life review helps people recollect past tomes of difficulty, and how they overcame it. These strength and successes can then be linked to current concerns, which increases coping skills.

MEDICATION CONCERNS

When assessing depression, always consider complications from over-medication, drug interactions, medication side-effects, and slowed or impaired metabolism.

Although cognitive therapy is helpful for depression, medication is often needed to get the resident well enough to respond to intervention. When it is decided to use medication to treat depression, make sure there is:

1. Adequate indication for its use

2. A proper dosage

3. An acceptable duration to assess effectiveness

4. Careful monitoring of side-effects

5. A positive response.

BIPOLAR DISORDER

Bipolar disorder, or *manic depression* is thought to have a strong biological component. The symptoms of this disorder include feelings of euphoria and irritability.

When a person is manic, speech is hurried, pressured, and never ending What the person says may make no sense at all. They may exhibit a condition known as *flight of ideas* where the talk about a series of unconnected thoughts. It's common for the person to have *delusions of grandeur,* the belief that one is all powerful, and to have unrealistic expectations of their ability. They have poor insight and judgement, and may make unrealistic business deals or spend all of their money recklessly. In addition, many manic people exhibit hyper-sexuality.

BEHAVIORAL INTERVENTIONS FOR BIPOLAR DISORDER

1. Do a drug screening to rule out drug-induced psychosis.

2. Rule out any other medical condition.

2. Provide a safe environment.

3. Orient the resident to reality and provide maximum autonomy.

4. Assess for harm to self and others.

5. Begin a medication regimen

GRIEF

Grief is a normal response to loss. Sadness and depression are part of the grieving process, and should not be considered a behavioral disorder. When a resident appears to be depressed, a *loss history* should be taken. This is an historical survey of the person's recent and remote losses. Losses can include te death of loved ones, but also can be the loss of a job, a pet, a limb, or social standing.

If it appears that the person is suffering from un-resolved grief, and the losses have been listed, the losses must be grieved.

One of the most effective ways to help people grieve is to explain the normal stages of grief to them, as it nor-malizes the emotions they are feeling, and allows them to take the time to work through and resolve the grief.

THE STAGES OF GRIEF

1. DENIAL

Denial is the reaction to the shock of loss.

The first reaction is, "No, this can't be true. This can't happen to me".

Getting stuck in denial results in the fantasy that the loss did not happen.

2. EMOTIONALITY

Once denial is broken through, an emotional roller coaster begins.

The emotional cycle runs from anger, to guilt, to sadness, and back to anger. Typical thoughts that accompany this are, "I'll show you... If only I'd..., You've hurt me"...I hate you."

Getting stuck in anger results in the persecution of the other. The person spends the rest of their life blaming the lost person for their misery.

Getting stuck in guilt can result in and endless persecution of one's self. As mentioned before, guilt ridden people often become convinced that they are evil, and would be better of dead.

3. BARGAINING

Bargaining is magical thinking. It's the fantasy that if you can just do or say the right thing, you can recover the loss.

Bargains may be made with one's self, with the lost person, or with God. Getting stuck in bargaining results in the obsession with the other. For example, some people maintain the belief that someday they will get a mate back, even when they may have remarried and started a new family.

4. DEPRESSION

Depression is the loss of the internal presence of the lost person or object.

This feels like a gaping black hole in the soul, and every moment feels like eternity. The depression stage feels as if it will last forever, but it doesn't.

Getting stuck in depression results in shutting down, withdrawal from the world, and isolation.

5. ACCEPTANCE

Acceptance is the realistic observation that the loss is permanent. It involves re-focusing on what was gained from the experience, and a reconnecting to the world.

The grieving process for a catastrophic loss can last well over a year. During this time, the person is at increased risk for suicide, illness, or a serious emotional breakdown. Allowing the person the opportunity to talk frequently about the loss speeds this healing process.

Chapter eight

SUICIDE

I never met George Burns, but I admired him. And I do know his goal was to put on a performance on his 100th birthday. Although he never made it, he and thousands of fans were looking forward to this event. And this is the important thing—at 99 he was still setting goals, still making plans. This is successful aging.

It's important to keep this in mind when working with an elderly suicidal person. Suicide is seldom a rational solution to life's problems. It is here that our unconscious bias against age may creep in and sit on our treatment plan.

When working with a suicidal person of thirty who loses their spouse, we think, "He's young, he needs to get over it. He has his whole life ahead of him."

We forget that an eighty-year-old *also has his whole life ahead of him*—it just may be a much shorter life. George lost Gracie many years ago. There is little doubt that it devastated him and that he grieved for years, but he never lost the lust for life.

Behavioral Objective

At the end of this section readers will be able to

Identify cues to suicidal ideation

Name the major suicide risk factors

Describe silent suicide

Assess a person for risk

Cues to suicide

Giving away a valued personal possessions

Putting personal and business affairs in order as though preparing to take a long journey

Inquiring about how one donates his/her body to a medical school

Planning his/her funeral shortly after the death of a loved one

A poor adjustment to the recent loss of one or more loved ones

A person who has always resisted suddenly composing a last will and testament

Writing a suicide note

A sudden unexplained recovery from a severe depression. (They may have resolved their problems by deciding to kill themselves)

Any unexplainable change in a usual behavioral pattern

Crying for no apparent reason

Poor sleeping habits

Loss of appetite

Loss of sex drive

Loss of ability to think

Having suicidal thoughts is not a normal phase of life—it is the will to live gone south for the winter. A suicidal person feels that things will never change. But although winter can seem bleak, cold, and never-ending, it eventually passes, and so do thoughts of suicide. Because of this, suicide has often been called a permanent solution to a temporary problem. It is, in fact, a maladaptive means to escape from anguish.

Suicide is currently the seventh leading cause of death in the United States. It accounts for over 24,000 deaths each year. And the suicide rate rises consistently as age increases—taking one's own life is presently the ninth leading cause of death in the elderly. White males over 65 have the highest suicide rate—twice the rate of the general population, and *six times* the rate in women over 65.

Elderly people actually have a lower incidence of suicide attempts than younger people, but they are much more intent on killing themselves, and therefore they have a much higher success rate. Nonfatal suicidal gestures are uncommon among the elderly. Unlike attempts by teens and other borderlines, suicide attempts in the elderly are rarely done for social manipulation —they are the direct intent to die. Lethal methods tend to be used, and failure to kill one's self is most often due to poor planning, rather than any lack of intent.

RISK FACTORS

Major depression is the most common reason for suicide—the suicide rate among the depressed being *four times* higher than the national average. When the person is suffering from psychotic depression, the rate is *five times* higher.

Any psychotic disorder increases risk—there are not

many old schizophrenics. A psychotic person who has paranoid thoughts, is inappropriately fearful and subject to panic states is at very high risk for self harm. This risk is increased even more if the person hears voices commanding him to kill himself.

Suicide is more common in the divorced and widowed. Elderly men who lose their wives are at highest risk. Oftentimes, the wife was responsible for social activities of the couple, and her death or departure means an abrupt end of social interaction.

The more closely a person is involved with others, the lower the probability of suicide. Therefore, it is important to look at the person's social support network when doing a suicide assessment. If the person has no friends or family, they are at high risk.

There is also a direct relationship between social status and suicide. In general, the higher one is on the socioeconomic ladder, the more likely they are to attempt suicide. For example, physicians and dentists have a much higher incidence of suicide than the general population.

Weakening of higher brain functions by sleeplessness, alcohol or drugs also strongly contributes to the potential for self-destruction. In fact, half of all suicides are associated with alcohol abuse, and the suicide rate among elderly alcoholics is *ten times* that of those who do not drink. About 70 percent of successful suicides in the elderly are committed by residents with a previous diagnosis of alcoholism, psychosis, or organic brain syndrome.

The incidence of suicide also rises after surgery. Particularly in surgeries that mutilate or change a person's appearance, the impact on the person's body image is

Suicide risk signals

Sudden Behavior Changes:
 insomnia
 anorexia
 social withdrawal
 substance abuse
 loss of interest inactivities.

Inability to talk about the future

Has no plans for next week or next month.

Has made suicidal threats

Perceives life situation as hopeless

Has no options for making changes.

Lack of Family and/or Peer Support
 (This can be either actual or perceived lack of support).

Predictors of suicide

Previous attempt

Single male over 65

Family History

Statements of intent

Alcohol or drug abuse

Significant loss

Purchase of a gun

Stockpiling medications

often intolerable. This loss must be grieved completely in order for the person to move ahead.

Suicide by a close family member increases one's suicide potential significantly. Guilt, especially over the dead relative, feelings of worthlessness, the wish for punishment, social withdrawal, and feelings of hopelessness, anxiety, and agitation are all contributing factors

However, the most important predictor of suicide is a *previous attempt*. Over half of those who commit suicide have had at least one previous attempt.

ANNOUNCING SUICIDE

Unfortunately, elderly suicidal people seldom seek help from mental health practitioners. But over 60 percent of those who do commit suicide tell others beforehand. In fact, the typical suicidal person will tell at least three people about their intent before they attempt it.

One of the people that they tell is often their physician. More than 65 percent of all suicide victims seek medical attention within three months before their suicide. Among successful suicides, 75 percent have contacted their physician within one month before their death, and over one third have seen a doctor just a week before their demise.

So, in fact, suicidal people almost always communicate their intent to kill themselves, and do it several times and in different ways. Communication may consist of overt statements of suicide, statements of not wanting to live, or statements that life is no longer worth living. Less direct methods of communication include making will under unusual circumstances, changing insurance policies, giving away valued objects, or making statements of, "putting my affairs in order."

Silent suicide is the intent to kill one's self by nonviolent means, often through self starvation and resistance to care. These attempts to end one's life often go unrecognized because the depression is not diagnosed, and resistance to care is seen as a bothersome behavioral problem rather than a suicide attempt. Because of this, resistance to care should always be considered as a sign of depression and suicidal intent (more information in this appears in the section of this book called *Resisting Care*).

BEHAVIORAL INTERVENTIONS FOR SUICIDE

1. Ask the person about their suicidal thoughts.

Suicide is seen as the only solution to what appears to be an unsolvable problem. Effective intervention consists of *identifying the problem*, and *helping he person see that there are more constructive solutions.*

2. Ask if the person has a plan.

A person with a plan and the means to carry it out is at extremely high risk.

3. Get a thorough history about depression and suicide from family members and friends.

If this person has a family history of suicide, SSRI's (such as Prozac) can be of great help. Studies show that suicide can have a genetic component, and low levels of serotonin are found in suicidal families.

4. Ask people with chronic pain about suicidal thoughts.

Factors leading to suicide

Acting out
Alcohol abuse
Arrested grief
Diminished life goals
Drug abuse
Conflicts with children
Chronic pain
Chronic illness
Depression
Disability
Financial problems
Fading recuperative power
Loneliness
Loss of spouse
Marital conflict
No social support system
Physical Illness
Poor physical health
Psychosis
Poor coping skills
Social isolation

Chronic, unremitting pain often leads to the wish to die. However, when pressed, most people with chronic pain will agree that what they really want is to *stop suffering*. Once this is established, all efforts should be focused on reducing the pain. A good pain management program can do wonders in these cases.

5. Assess their social support network, and the activities of a current typical day.

A day spent with no friends and no joy is a day wasted. Help the person plan a day of enjoyment, and explore ways of connecting them with others who share similar interests.

6. The most effective treatment of suicide in the elderly involves cognitive therapy and group therapy, often combined with medication.

Successful treatment occurs when the suicidal person comes to see that there are other ways to deal with their feelings and their problems. The suicidal elderly person needs to be reconnected to the world, and given a purpose to live. Ferreting out this purpose is the core of cure.

Old age should be a time of enjoyment, creativity and social gratification. When the barriers of pain and suffering are removed, life regains meaning. Catastrophic losses in life do not inevitably lead to the loss of the will to live. Like Mr. Burns, the well adjusted elderly never lose this feeling. Say good night, Gracie.

Chapter nine

ANXIETY

Fear is a normal human emotion. And although no one enjoys the feeling of fear, it has an important function— to help us avoid danger.

It's normal to be afraid of something we have never encountered before. Fear prompts us to proceed with caution when we enter unexplored territory, and only when we feel that we can handle a situation does the fear disappear.

Fear has another important function—it promotes social bonding. All children are naturally afraid to be alone. Because children can't survive without their parents, fear saves their life. A child who had no fear would wander off, and probably die.

Kids automatically run to their parents whenever they get scared. The parent's natural tendency is to calm the child and allay the fears.

In this way, fear teaches us how to cope. As we hear our mother's voice say, "It's all right, nothing will hurt you now," over and over, we eventually make these words a part of ourselves. This process of internalizing

Behavioral Objectives

At the end of this section readers will be able to:

Define the functions of anxiety

Differentiate between anxiety disorders and grief reactions

List the medical causes of anxiety

Describe symptoms and causes of panic attacks

Causes of organic anxiety disorders

Endocrine disorders

Hypo- and hyper-thyroidism

Pheochromocytoma (an adrenalin secreting tumor)

Hypoglycemia

Hypercortisolism

Stimulants
  caffeine
  cocaine
  amphetamines
  nicotine

Withdrawal from sedatives, alcohol, or tranquilizers

Brain Tumors

Strokes

Epilepsy

Pulmonary embolus

Chronic pulmonary disease

Aspirin intolerance

Collagen vascular disease

Brucellosis (undulant fever, rock fever, and Malta fever)

B_{12} deficiency

Demyelinating disease

Heavy metal intoxication

Food allergies

Balance disorder

calming messages is called *self-soothing.*

Although we spend most of our early years physically and emotionally attached to our mothers, as we grow and mature, and learn to self-soothe, we are able to tolerate more and more time alone. We also come to realize that many of the things we fear will never happen—there are no monsters in the closet.

Anxiety disorders occur because of the failure of both of these factors— people with anxiety disorders are afraid to be alone, and they have never learned to self-soothe. In these cases, older people may become overly dependent on others and engage in incessant attention seeking. They may also become overly demanding. But they also have another deficit—they cannot separate *realistic* fears from *irrational* fears

The sudden beginning of anxiety disorders is unusual in elderly people, but many have had a long standing history of anxiety disorders. In addition, loss provokes fear—it makes elderly people afraid to form new friendships.

Anxiety can be a symptom of mental illness such as depression, psychosis, or dementia. But it can also be a symptom of physical illness such as organ failure or delirium. For example, many people with COPD exhibit anxiety. Anxiety can also be the result of stressful life circumstances such as environmental changes, financial problems, or unresolved grief and loss.

ANXIETY DISORDERS AND GRIEF

Most elderly people have experienced multiple losses. The normal response to loss is grief. Normally grief is a time limited reaction, But sometimes grief reactions become chronic and interfere with long-term functioning. This type of problem is called *pathological grief.*

Grief can have an immediate or delayed onset. Delayed onset occurs when the person gets stuck in the stage of denial. Delayed grief reactions, therefore, are somewhat similar to the symptoms of Post Traumatic Stress Disorder, and should be considered an anxiety disorder. Pathological grief differs from normal grief in the development of *anxious apprehension, phobias, panic, and depression.*

Most societies have mourning rituals and ceremonies that surround the death or loss of a close member of the family. These rituals create a context in which all the bereaved relatives and friends can experience their painful emotions and work through their loss. However, these rituals and ceremonies no longer exist in much of American culture, and because of this, it's difficult or impossible for most people to do proper grief work.

Because of the loss of formal ritual, many people in our culture are actually unaware that they must mourn or grieve. Instead, they try to escape from their pain and carry on as usual. When this occurs, the buried feelings may erupt later, disguised in some other form—often in the form of panic attacks and anxiety symptoms.

The human grief response has its origins early in mankind's social evolution. For example, crying is an important survival mechanism. A small child separated from the tribe could be found by listening to their cries. The children that cried the most were the ones that were found the easiest. After thousands of years of development and evolution, crying when faced with loss has become a fundamental human instinct.

To help work through loss, traditional mourning

Anxiety disorders

Panic Disorder

Agoraphobia

Social phobia

Simple phobia

Obsessive Compulsive disorder

Post Traumatic Stress Disorder

Generalized Anxiety Disorder

Organic anxiety disorder

rituals in other cultures encourage loud and sustained crying and the expression of painful emotions. After a few days of this, emotional exhaustion is experienced, it then becomes possible for the bereaved person to complete the emotional and cognitive aspects of the grieving process

Failure to mourn results in suppression of the anger, the fear, and the related emotions in the grief process. Because these emotions never get expressed, the levels of arousal in the person remain persistently high. After the loss, the bereaved person may carry on with his usual daily activities. But even though a grieving person may have successfully suppressed their grief, their body is still experiencing the grief reaction.

Symptoms may not appear until many years after the loss. When they do appear, it's frequently on or around the anniversary of the loss. The most common symptoms are panic attacks and phobias.

On occasion, the loss of one's health can becomes a substitute for the loss of the person. Instead of grieving, the person becomes preoccupied with phobias, panic attacks, or illness. The search for the cure for the illness unconsciously represents a search for the lost relative. Feelings of anger and rage are then displaced into the doctors and caregivers who fail to find a cure.

Even if it is suggested that the anxiety disorder is a result of unresolved grief, the patients are very reluctant to engage in grief work. To make things even more difficult, the spouse or family members may ridicule the idea of grief work, claiming it is irrelevant to the problem. If the patient does begin grief work, family will often interfere with the process and ridicule them for weeping and crying. If this occurs, the treatment must be explained thoroughly to family members, and the family must be involved in the treatment process

BEHAVIORAL INTERVENTIONS FOR ANXIETY

1. Rule out medication and physical problems.

2. Explore the possibility of grief reaction.

3. Look for secondary gain.

4. Teach abdominal breathing.

5. Note any situations in the facility that trigger anxiety.

6. Eliminate caffeine and other stimulants.

7. Teach problem solving and coping skills.

PANIC ATTACKS

Elderly people often suffer from panic attacks, which they mistake for heart attacks. Many emergency room visits are for bouts of panic.

If you have ever had a panic attack, you know that it feels awful You are overwhelmed by fear, and convinced that you are going to die.

These attacks should always be checked out carefully. If it is determined that they have no biological cause, they should be dealt with through behavioral intervention.

INTERVENTIONS FOR PANIC ATTACKS

1. The person should be educated about panic attacks—what causes them, what they

are, and what they feel like.

Panic attacks usually begin with the perception of an unusual physical symptom (for example, a sudden pain). This is followed by an irrational conclusion ("I have a terrible disease, and I'm going to die). The reaction to this conclusion is panic. Teach the person to recognize this process, and help them self soothe when they feel the symptoms.

3. **Explain clearly that although panic attacks feel terrible, *they are completely harmless*.**

Often, when the person understands this, the attacks stop.

4. **Teach deep breathing,**

This aborts the attack.

MEDICATION FOR ANXIETY

Medication should be considered only when all other interventions have failed. Tranquilizers are *not* recommended for long term use in the elderly because of their potential for abuse and because they exacerbate cognitive problems. They also have psychomotor effects that lead to adverse events such as falls, and they are addictive. I have found that it's much more difficult to get a person off tranquilizers than it is to treat anxiety behaviorally.

Chapter ten

MEDICAL PROBLEMS

Probably the biggest difference between treating emotional and behavioral problems in younger people and in the elderly is that most elderly people are also suffering from *multiple medical problems.*

Psychological problems in this population are often indicators of physical illness. In fact, more than half of all older psychiatric patients have an undetected physical illness.

A troubling finding in geriatric mental health assessment is that almost 80 percent of physical illnesses are missed by psychiatrists during the initial assessment. This happens in part because mental health practitioners are trained to look symptoms as signs of psychopathology, not medical illness.

The reality is that medical problems can cause serious behavioral and emotional disorders, and these factors should always be considered before any diagnosis or behavioral intervention is attempted.

A medical history should be the first step in any diagnosis. It should include a history of all illnesses, injuries, and hospitalizations throughout the person's

Behavioral Objectives

After completing this section readers will be able to

Understand the role that illness plays in the problems plaguing today's rapidly growing elderly population

Assess the effects of illness on mental health

Recognize the causes and consequences of medical illness in behavioral and emotional disturbances in the elderly

Use new knowledge and skills to improve the quality of life of the elderly and all who care for them lifespan. Unfortunately, this is often impossible, as medical records are lost, and family members are unavailable. Often, the only data available is from the person himself, and they may have forgotten many of their illnesses, injuries and aliments.

To further complicate things, the signs and symptoms of many diseases are often less severe, non-specific, or not present in many elders. People suffering form these disorders may not be able to give you an accurate description of what they are experiencing. The best you might get form a person is that they feel tired, or they are "not themselves."

Medical disorders may also present themselves as confusion of functional decline. These things may be mistaken for normal aging, while they are, in fact, masking a serious problem.

MEDICATION

Most people take any medication that their doctor recommends without question. The majority of the people I work with don't know the names of the medicines they are taking, or why they are taking them.

Each year, adverse reactions to prescription drugs, drug misuse, and medication abuse account for thousands of illnesses and deaths in the elderly.

An adverse reaction is an unexpected and unwanted response to a drug that results in illness, organ failure or death. Drug *misuse* is the under use, overuse, improper use or erratic use of a medication. Drug *abuse* is the use of a drug for other than its intended purpose.

It's important to understand that any drug that has a therapeutic affect can also have an adverse effect on a person. Unfortunately up to 90 percent of people over 65 will suffer side-effects from medication at some time in their life.

The medical community has not done an effective job in tackling this problem. Almost 65 percent of elders are not told by their doctors about precautions in using medications, and 67 percent are not told anything about possible side-effects.

In many cases the prescribing physician did not know about the potential adverse effects of the medication, and were not aware of the interactive effects it could have with other medications the patient was taking. Older people are more prone to idiosyncratic reactions to medicines, and drugs should always be considered as a potential cause of cognitive or behavioral problems.

Drugs act differently in older people. The loss of brain cells and the lower amounts of neurotransmitters in the older brain can amplify the effects of many medications, and doses that are safe for younger people are often toxic in the aged.

Older bodies take much longer to metabolize and excrete certain drugs. Decreased liver and kidney function increase the risk of drug toxicity. In short, all medications should be given with care and closely monitored. In many cases dosages need to be decreased.

For these reasons any symptom in an elderly patient should be considered to be a drug side-effect until proven otherwise.

In his book, *The People's Pharmacy,* Joe Graeden claims that thousands of cases of confusion, mood disorders and memory problems are actually a result of the toxic effects of over-medication. He calls this problem the "spaced-out Grandma syndrome."

Common side effects of drugs

Depression

antibiotics
ulcer medications
steroids
anti-glaucoma eye drops
cardiovascular drugs
anti-Parkinson's drugs
anti-epileptic medications
Advil
Naprosyn
Indocin (for arthritis)
Antabuse
Hytrin (for benign prostatic hyperplasia)

Psychosis

antibiotics
urinary tract infection drugs
analgesics
 aspirin
 Darvon
cold medicines
 Actifed
 Benadryl
Albuterol (for asthma)
cardiovascular medications
antidepressants
tranquilizers
Vincristine (for cancer)
Sinemet (anti-Parkinson's)

Common side effects of drugs

Confusion & Delirium

antibiotics
steroids
antihistamines
insulin
Tagamet
antidepressants,
Haldol
Thorazine
barbiturates
hypnotics
tranquilizers
analgesics
neurologic medications

Dementia

Zantac
Axid
Pepcid
cardiovascular drugs
central nervous system drugs

Insomnia

antibiotics
amantadine
Sudafed
gastrointestinal drugs
Inderal.
drugs containing caffeine
drugs containing ephedrine

Over-medication is a very common problem. One woman who came to see me was taking seventeen prescription medications! These drugs were given to her by several doctors for various ailments she had suffered over a period of years, but it seemed that no one had ever asked her if she was taking any other medication. Furthermore, none of the doctors told her when to stop taking the medication, so she continued to take medicine for ailments that had disappeared long ago.

Over a third of elderly people make serious mistakes in taking their medication—either forgetting to take it, or forgetting that they have taken it, and therefore over-dosing.

Even worse, about 12 percent of people taking prescription drugs are using medications that were actually prescribed for someone else. They accidentally take medicine that is not their own because they can't read the label, or because they got it from a friend who said it "worked for them."

Although most people don't realize it, many over-the-counter medications can also significantly interfere with memory, mood, and thinking. But even so,, few if any of these medications indicate cognitive impairment as a side-effect. Doctors don't often explain to their patients that the drug they are prescribing may have an effect on their memory or thinking.

This is not a small problem. In fact, it is estimated that over 200,000 people in this country are currently suffering from medication-induced mental problems.

In addition to experiencing problems with drugs, many people resort to alternative medicines, vitamins, herbs and other over-the-counter drugs to help them with their various maladies. This becomes problematic because most people don't let anyone know what they are taking.

Always ask the person to tell you about everything they are taking. Ask them about prescription drugs, non-prescription drugs, vitamins, herbs, nutrients, and other alternative remedies. Ask them about any allergic reactions or adverse symptoms they have experienced in the past. If you don't ask, you will not be told.

If you are dispensing medicine, always tell people what medications they are about to take, and what the potential side effects are. If you don't know what they are, look it up. Telling the person about the medicine can avert allergic or toxic reactions.

DRUG ABUSE

Substance abuse among the elderly is a very common but often undetected problem. Even though the elderly are at highest risk for drug misuse and abuse, the problem is chronically under-diagnosed. When misuse rather than abuse is suspected, education and clear instructions about the use of the medication may be all that is needed. Commonly misused prescription drugs include sedative-hypnotics (sleeping pills), anti-anxiety agents (such as valium and xanax), and analgesics (such as oxicodone). In these cases drug education groups can be a valuable tool. When a person is abusing a drug, however, things get more complicated

Diazepam (Valium), codeine, meprobamate (Miltown), and flurazepam (Dalmane) are the top four drugs of abuse. There is 60 percent correlation between prescription drug abuse and alcoholism.

Although it is not well known to the public, alcohol related problems cause as many deaths as heart attacks.

Common side effects of psychotropic medications

Autonomic nervous system effects

orthostatic hypotension
dizziness
imbalance upon standing
falls
confusion
lethargy
daytime sleepiness

Oversedation & hypotension
slurred speech
staggering
fainting
dizziness or falling

Sedation
drowsiness
impaired concentration
slowed reaction time

Effects on the eye
increased sensitivity to light
strange pigmentation
increased lens cloudiness

Problems Associated with Amputation

Pain
Phantom pain
Balance
Gait
Blood Pressure
Grief
Body image disturbance
Neuropathy
Depression
Cognitive impairment

It is estimated that between two and ten percent of individuals over the age of 60 suffer from alcoholism. In a survey of elderly patients in Washington, 9.6 percent were diagnosed with alcohol abuse, while about 5 percent were referred for prescription drug abuse.

Psychosocial factors such as loneliness and depression, and health factors related to the aging process, such as pain, disability, or chronic disease are the major contributors to alcoholism and drug abuse in older people.

A thorough assessment is essential to detect and correct drug misuse and to diagnose drug abuse. Prior to considering any medication, the attending staff should screen the person for abuse by asking about an individual or family history of alcohol or other drug abuse. Care givers should also learn to recognize drug-seeking behaviors.

When medication is used, there should be a *clear clinical indication* and a *therapeutic end-point and time limit.*

DIALYSIS

While it is important to be aware that while there are many people who have medical causes for mental illness, almost everyone has strong emotional responses to physical illness.

People undergoing dialyses face many challenges First they must cope with the loss of function of their kidneys. This is a devastating loss which is often accompanied by a great deal of anxiety, depression and grieving. Second, dialysis means adopting an entirely new lifestyle—one in which several days a week are devoted to dialysis. Third, a majority of people in dialysis feel exhausted after the procedure, and cannot do anything strenuous the rest of the day, Fourth they must accept strict dietary restrictions to maintain their health, The incidence of depression is very high among dialysis patients, and a depression screening should be routine in this population. About one in ten people undergoing dialysis choose to end their lives by discontinuing treatment.

Dialysis patients also have a high incidence of sleep apnea, which causes cognitive problems and exacerbates fatigue.

Dialysis patients are at risk for thiamine deficiency, which may mimic symptoms of dementia. In rare cases dialysis can result in a toxic buildup of alum-inum in the brain, which results in dementia-like symptoms (sometimes called *dialysis dementia*). This occurs over time in areas where the water supply contains high levels of aluminum. Although this is a fairly well known phenomenon, it's often overlooked or missed. Untreated, it is often fatal.

POST-SURGICAL BEHAVIORAL PROBLEMS

Elderly people often undergo surgery, and although most of these surgeries go well, it is not uncommon to see drastic behavioral changes after their return from the hospital. The trauma of surgery itself always causes a significant amount of stress. The most common problems associated with surgery are:

Adjustment disorder

Post-surgical depression

Post-surgical psychosis

Biochemical and metabolic imbalances (for example, blood pressure changes after amputation)

Problems with memory and thinking after surgery

Symptoms of Constipation

Behavioral Symptoms:

Fatigue
Lethargy
Irritability
Restlessness
Quarrelsome
Intolerant
Lack of endurance

Physical symptoms:

Shoulder Pain
Generalized Pain
Fever
Headache
Vomiting
Nutrient malabsorption
Malodorous stool
Poor digestion
Faulty metabolism

Diseases of the colon:

Sigmoid flexure
Fissures
Fistulas
Hemorrhoids
Diverticulitis
Malignancies
Impaction

Interventions for urinary incontinence

Limit fluid intake at night
(no fluids after 7 p.m.)

Reduce the consumption of
caffeinated beverages and
alcohol
(both irritate the bladder)

Re-evaluate medications
(some may trigger
incontinence)

Elevate feet for a few hours
before bed
(reduces night time urination)

Check for a urinary tract
infection
(antibiotics can cure
this incontinence)

Use pelvic floor exercises
(Kegel exercises:) along with
biofeedback to strengthen the
pelvic muscles
(helps both urge and stress
incontinence)

Establish a urination schedule
(for urge incontinence)

Surgery to resuspend the
bladder

also occur because of several factors. Caloric demand, the amount of energy consumed by the body, often increases as the body tries to heal itself. If nutrition isn't adequate, the brain is most often the first organ to suffer.

Sometimes tiny clots are thrown during and after the surgery, which may result in minor strokes, and consequently impair brain function.

Older people may also fail to metabolize the anesthetic properly. The effects of anesthetic can often linger for weeks after surgery, and can disrupt the person's ability to function.

In addition, being anesthetized for hours may causes *anoxia* (oxygen starvation) which can lead to diffuse brain damage, causing memory and behavioral problems.

BODY IMAGE PROBLEMS

Unfortunately, many elderly residents undergo the loss of a limb or the loss of the function of a limb. Losing a limb is a traumatic and devastating process. As well as altering the person's ability to function normally in the world, the loss of a limb changes a person's body image and sense of self. They no longer feel normal; they no longer feel accepted.

These feelings are made worse by the reactions that others have to the injury. Many people find amputations frightening, and avoid looking at a person with a missing limb. In their efforts to cope with their fear of rejection, the person may become withdrawn, or lash out at others, feeling that by rejecting others, they can save themselves from being rejected.

During this time, the person may be difficult to work with—they may be uncooperative, unpleasant and abusive. It's important to keep this in mind when working with a person who has lost a limb.

It is normal for a person to go through a period of grieving for their missing limb. But they are often reluctant to discuss their feelings with others. Addressing the issue head on is often the best way to opening the avenue to communication. A statement such as, "Last year I was working with a lady who lost her leg. She told me it was a very difficult time for her. I wonder if you might be feeling that way too."

Other problems accompany amputations. Blood pressure may be altered. Balance and gait may be affected. And phantom-limb pain may cause discomfort and anxiety.

POST-STROKE DEPRESSION

Depression is a common consequence of stroke. This is particularly true if the stroke has resulted in permanent disability. The patient often loses much of his independence, and also suffers from body image difficulties previously discussed.

If the person has lost the ability to speak, things are even worse. Loss of the ability to communicate is a devastating loss, and often results in complete withdrawal.

It is very useful in these cases to get a complete speech and language assessment.

> Several years ago I was asked to see a man who had been suffering from severe depression. Three years prior he had suffered a stroke that left him completely unable to speak. His ability to think, how-ever, had been untouched.
>
> I ordered an *augmented communication screening,* an assessment that determined his ability to use a speech synthesizer (which in this case was a computer that contained a program to reproduce speech). When he received the device, his world

Geriatric lab values

Chemistry (serum)

Calcium	8.9 mg-10.9 mg/100 ml (to 11 mg for patients under 70)
Chloride	96 mEq-110 mEq/L
Cholesterol (total)	160 mg-300 mg/100 ml (150 mg-250 mg/100 ml for patients under 70)
Glucose (fasting)	52 mg-140 mg/100 ml
Phosphorus	.1 mg-5.1 mgi100 mi
Potassium	3.0 mEq-5.9 mEq/L
Protein (total)	5.3 g-7.8 g/100 ml
Protein (albumin)	3.0 g-5.0 g/100 ml (to 5.6 g/100 ml for patients under 70)
Sodium	136 mEq-142 mEq/L
Urea nitrogen (BUN)	7.0 mg-35.0 mgi100 mi
Uric acid	2.0 mg-9.2 mgi100 mi

Chemistry (Urine)

Creatinine	0.4 mg-1.9 mg/100 ml

Creatinine clearance must be calculated to take into account age related decrease in glomerular filtration rate:

$$* \frac{140\text{-age}) \times \text{body weight (kg)}}{\text{serum creatinine} \times 72 \text{ kg}}$$

Endocrinology

TSH	0.3-6.3 IU/ml

Geriatric lab values

Enzymes

Alanine aminotransferase (ALT)	0-22 units (to 36 units for patients under 70)
Aspartate aminotransferase (AST)	5-40 units
Phosphatase (alkaline)	19.9 -83.4 units
Phosphatase (acid)	0.0 -1.6 units

Hematology

Hemoglobin	9 g-17 g/100 ml (to 18 g for patients under 70)
Hematocrit	35% - 54%
Red blood cells	3,000,000/mm^3 - 5,000,000/mm^3
White blood cells	3,100/mm^3 - 12,700 mm^3

changed. For the first time in years, he was able to speak again. That was the end of his depression.

FAILURE TO THRIVE

Studies show that about 15percent of older people require professional intervention for *failure to thrive*. This condition includes a decline in physical health, weight loss, loss of appetite, and social withdrawal in the absence of any obvious cause. Along with the physical decline there is often depression, anxiety and confusion.

DEHYDRATION

Several years ago I was called in to see an 80 year old women named Madeline. She had recently become confused, disoriented, and was beginning to show some signs of dementia. In the course of the interview, it was discovered that she was drinking very little fluids. When fluids were increased, the symptoms went away within three days.

Since that time I have observed that a great many elderly people do not drink enough water. In some cases this is because they have lost their sense of thirst. But after asking dozens of people why they don't drink water, he answer I get the most is, "Because it makes me pee."

And they are right. The decreased fluid intake reduces their need to urinate. Incontinence is often a source of shame and inconvenience, and not drinking reduces the problem. Unfortunately, it also causes fluid and electrolyte imbalances in the brain, and can cause dementia-like symptoms. Very often, correcting incontinence problems eliminates dehydration, and thus eliminates behavioral problems.

NUTRITIONAL PROBLEMS

Another potential cause of behavioral problems in inadequate or poorly balanced nutrition. As people age, they often lose their sense of smell and taste which decreases their enjoyment of food.

They also may lose their sense of hunger. It has been found that the biochemical imbalances that cause anorexia in younger people and changes in the natural aging of the brain are very similar. Drug withdrawal and depression may also cause geriatric anorexia. The consequence of these changes leads to inadequate intake of calories and essential nutrients.

Elderly people also have a tendency to narrow the scope of what they will eat, and therefore may become deficient in certain vitamins and minerals. Many elderly people are deficient in the B vitamins.

As mentioned above, other people may overload themselves with nutritional supplements, in the hope that taking mega-doses of certain nutrients will keep them young and healthy forever. It's a good idea to ask about the nutritional supplements, herbs, and other self medicating behavior the person is engaged in, as this is very common, and will not be mentioned unless you inquire. Supplements are not an alternative to proper eating.

Sadly, failure to thrive, to drink or to eat may also be the result of neglect at home. I have worked with families that literally starved their partners to death. A typical case of neglect was described by Christine Williams-Burgess and Mary Kay Kimball.

> Mr. R. arrived in the emergency room with a questionable new stroke. He was dehydrated and had lost 50 pounds. He was unable to walk and was incontinent of urine and stool.

Drugs Causing or Aggravating Esophageal Reflux

Anticholinergics
R-agonists
Calcium channel blockers
Nicotine
Nitrates
NSAIDS
Antiparkinsonians
Estrogen
Tricyclic antidepressants
Iron salts
Morphine/meperidine
Theophylline

During assessment the patient confided that he felt he was a burden to his wife. He was embarrassed regarding his loss of continence and felt badly that his wife "had to clean him like a baby."

Mrs. R. thought that Mr. R. was doing this on purpose. Thus, she would restrict food and fluids to decrease the frequency of the episodes of incontinence.

Cases of neglect like this often come to light when a patient improves rapidly in the hospital, and again deteriorates when returned home.

METABOLIC IMBALANCES

Minor illness, such as the flu, dietary habits, tobacco or alcohol use, and others factors that can affect lab values are more likely to affect test results among the elderly. The geriatric ranges shown in the margin are guidelines to help pinpoint causes of cognitive impairment. But even though lab values outside of these ranges should be considered as red flags for diagnoses, they do not necessarily indicate an abnormality, nor do results within these ranges necessarily rule it out.

HEAD TRAUMA

Being knocked unconscious can cause a *closed head injury*. This condition is caused by the bruising or tearing of delicate brain tissue. The brain is a jelly-like substance that is suspended in a bath of spinal fluid. It is protected by rubbery membranes called the *meninges*. Minor bumps on the head do not usually cause any damage. But getting hit hard enough to cause a loss of consciousness can cause serious injury to the brain=s delicate tissues.

A *concussion* is a temporary loss of consciousness occurring after a blow to the head. The impact of the blow causes the semi-liquid brain tissue to slosh about inside the skull, causing it to bruise. Like any bruise, the injured tissue then swells. When the brain becomes bruised and swollen, brain function can be disrupted for weeks after the injury. This can cause loss of memory, and sometimes permanent brain damage.

In younger people, most concussions are caused by traffic accidents, but in the elderly they can also occur from falls, or from being hit on the head by any object.

Immediately after a concussion, the victim may experience confusion, memory loss, vomiting, and blurred vision. The longer the person is unconscious, the more severe the symptoms tend to be.

As soon as possible after a person has experienced a loss of consciousness, she should see a doctor to rule out skull fracture, brain injury, or bleeding inside the lining of the brain called *subdural hematoma*. Subdural bleeding is a serious condition that requires immediate medical attention. Weeks after a head injury, the person may experience headaches, dizziness, changes in behavior, drowsiness, and memory loss.

About one-third of the people who experience a concussion will exhibit *post concussion syndrome*. This syndrome includes chronic memory loss, dizziness, and changes in behavior that can last over a year. Because most knocks on the head are soon forgotten, the person usually does not connect the symptoms with the accident.

Repeated concussions, such as those experienced by boxers, can cause permanent brain damage, including a condition called *punch drunk syndrome*. One study revealed that 87 percent of former boxers showed evidence of brain damage. We also know that a significant number of those suffering from dementia have a history of head injury.

Elderly people often bump their head and later forget that the incident happened. In a younger person, these bumps may be unimportant. But the brains of elderly people are sometimes smaller, and slosh about inside the skull more easily. The decreased amount of neurons in the elderly brain makes minor damage more serious. Even minor bumps on the head in the elderly, such as a bump on the head from a cabinet door, can cause subdural hematoma. Any bump on the head should be checked thoroughly.

DIZZINESS

Dizziness is a common complaint. However, it's been my experience that most people don't really mean that they are dizzy. A great many people who complain of dizziness are actually suffering from Parkinsonian difficulties, that is, if they lose their balance, they cannot regain it, and they may fall. Others use the word dizzy to describe muscle weakness or damage that results in unsteadiness, and causes the person to fall or bump into things.

Some people are actually feeling the results of *orthostatic hypotension,* a sudden drop in blood pressure upon standing. This means that when they stand up too quickly, they feel faint. This drop in blood pressure can be caused by medications or chronic low blood volume. Low blood pressure can also be a sign of internal blood loss, which is a serious condition. Still others are dizzy because of *vestibular disorders*—malfunctions in the balance apparatus in the ear that result feelings that the room is spinning around. Also known as *vertigo*, this can cause nausea and panic attacks. This can be caused by ear infections or damage to the balance organs themselves.

Chapter eleven

PAIN

It's three twenty-seven am when the phone rings. You are suddenly jolted out of a sound sleep. As you stagger towards the phone, your toe smashes against the suitcase you left on the floor.

The pain is intense and immediate. As you shout something X-rated, you hop about in agony. You sit down and rub your damaged digit, and thankfully in a few moments, the pain is gone.

Acute pain is useful in that it warns us that the body has sustained damage. The distress accompanies pain causes us to withdraw from the source of the pain, and teaches us to avoid similar situations in the future. It's your brain telling you, "Don't do that again!" If tissue injury occurs, pain motivates us to seek help. It also tells us to remain immobile so that healing can occur.

However, *chronic pain*, also called *unproductive pain*, is not useful in any way. It only serves to diminish the quality of life. The distress from chronic pain serves only to make the person suffer. Chronic pain can sap enjoyment from a day, and eventually hamper one's will

Behavioral objectives

At the end of this section resders will be able to

Describe the differences between acute and chronic pain

Define and differentiate pain tolerance from pain threshold

Discuss the relationship between pain and depression

Conduct a pain assessment

to live.

Pain in the elderly can cause impaired activities of daily living, depression, anxiety, lowered tolerance for frustration, problems with thinking and attention, sleep disturbances, and irritability.

Unfortunately, about one out of five elderly people suffer from chronic pain, and in nursing homes, the incidence of chronic pain can be as high as 80 percent.

Although the elderly are more prone to painful illnesses such as neuropathy, trigeminal neuralgia, spinal degeneration, arthritis, and a variety of other degenerative diseases, there is actually little evidence that pain complaints are more common in the normal aged. But despite this evidence, the fallacy persists that pain is an inevitable consequence of aging.

Unfortunately, the belief that all older people complain about pain can cause care givers to ignore complaints of pain and sometimes overlook serious pathology, including life-threatening illnesses. Pain and suffering should never be equated with the processes of normal aging, but should be treated in an older person just as it is in the young.

In reality, elderly people may actually under-report pain because they too expect pain with aging. In addition, those with communication difficulties or confusion may be unable to make others aware that they are in pain.

Interestingly, although cognitive impairment may be a barrier to pain assessment, it is important to recognize that even cognitively impaired residents reliably report the presence of pain when they are asked.

DEFINING PAIN

Unfortunately for care givers, pain is a completely subjective experience—there simply is no reliable way to objectively observe whether someone is in pain. Because of this, the most useful definition is, "pain is whatever a person says it is, and exists whenever he or she says it does." Because pain cannot be observed, proved or disproved, the only basis for pain assessment is the patient's subjective report that they are in pain

In the 1986 edition of *Cancer Pain Relief,* the World Health Organization states unequivocally, "Believe the patient's complaints of pain." In other words, a report of pain by a patient should be sufficient to establish pain as a diagnosis. This means that it is the person reporting the pain, and not the healthcare team nor the family who is the final authority on the reality of pain.

THE CAUSES OF PAIN

Another common misconception among health care professionals is the belief that all pain must have an *identifiable physical cause*. Because we like to believe we have control, we believe that if a person has pain, there is must be an observable cause. If we can't find the cause, we inaccurately conclude that the person has no "real" pain. However, *all* pain is real, regardless of its cause and regardless of whether it can be diagnosed or measured.

Lack of a physical diagnosis causes some people to conclude that a person's pain is *psychogenic* or "all in their head." However, purely psychogenic pain is extremely rare and should never be assumed merely because of the lack of ability to find a physical cause.

Because of this widespread belief that all pain should

be diagnosable, when there is difficulty establishing a cause for pain, the sufferers themselves may begin to question their own sanity. They may begin to fear they will be perceived as lying or malingering, and that pain relief will be withheld because their pain is not real. For this reason, it's useful to tell your patient's that all pain is real, and will be recognized as such.

The reality is that pain includes both a physical and an emotional component. To have pain that is purely physical, that is, to experience pain without distress, is very rare. Therefore, feelings of fear and anxiety are appropriate reactions to pain, and shouldn't be seen a evidence that the pain isn't "real."

LYING ABOUT PAIN

The reporting of pain by someone who is not actually suffering is called *malingering.* A true malingerer consciously fakes pain in order to get medication or to gain attention from family members or the healthcare staff. But even though many care givers believe that lying about pain is common, research shows that it is actually very rare.

When a person says they are in pain, care givers sometimes feel the need to decide whether they should believe a person who on other occasions has been untrustworthy. Although there is no accurate test to detect a malingerer, and in some cases we may disbelieve a person who claims to be in pain, professional responsibility dictates that we believe all patients who state that they are in pain. It is better to treat a malingerer than to deny treatment to someone who is suffering.

A professional assessment of pain should never include your personal biases, beliefs, values, or feelings about the person. It is also unacceptable to withhold appropriate treatment from a person in pain merely because you don't like them, don't believe them, or disapprove of their behavior.

All this being said, the social context in which the pain is occurring should be considered. *Secondary gain* from chronic pain, that is, the rewards one reaps from complaining of pain, includes increased attention from staff and family. In fact, in some cases, families and care givers unwittingly encourage a *sick role* in a person, attending to them when they complain and ignoring them when they don't.

For others, the expression of pain may be an attempt to cope with loneliness, fear of physical deterioration, or fear of impending death. Focusing on pain allows the person to avoid thinking about these unpleasant and frightening things. In these cases, behavioral intervention can be helpful.

PAIN BEHAVIOR

Many health care professionals have been taught to look for visible physiological and behavioral signs that accompany pain, and therefore can be used as the basis for objective pain assessment.

With acute pain, physiological signs include elevated blood-pressure, rapid heart beat, rapid breathing, dilated pupils and behaviors such as grimacing, moaning and flailing about.

However, with chronic pain, physical and behavioral adaptation occurs, resulting in periods where the person may show no overt signs of pain. As the body adapts to pain, after a period of time vital signs normalize. This return to equilibrium is necessary to prevent physical harm and stress on the body, but it does not necessarily mean the pain has disappeared.

When care givers follow the acute pain model to assess pain, there will be times when a patient's behavior and physical signs do not correlate with the patient's report of pain. Patients may experience even severe pain without acting like they are in pain. *In other words, lack of pain behavior doesn't mean lack of pain.*

A recent study shows the effect that behavior can have on pain assessment. In the study, nurses were told to rate the pain of two patients recovering from identical surgical procedures. Although the surgeries were identical, one of the patients smiled, while the other grimaced. Even though their behavior was different, the patients both reported that they had exactly the same amount of pain.

Lack of pain behavior doesn't mean lack of pain

Interestingly, in *both* cases, many of the nurses underestimated the amount of pain the patents reported, but the estimates were even lower for the smiling patient. This indicated that the nurses had relied on their expectations of the patient's pain and his behavior and appearance rather than on the person's actual report of his level of pain.

PAIN THRESHOLD

A person's *pain threshold* is the point at which a stimulus is perceived as painful. Many care giving professionals mistakenly believe that everyone perceives pain the same. In addition, over time, seasoned health-care workers often develop their own conclusions about the range of expected pain responses for certain situations. This can cause problems because a patient who experiences more pain than expected with a certain treatment, diagnostic procedure, or in a postoperative recovery period can become labeled as "exaggerating" their pain.

For example, surveys show that most nurses expect that the most severe pain following surgery will occur in the first 48 hours and then gradually subside. However, in a recent study of post-surgical patients, 31percent reported significant pain after the fourth postoperative day.

TOLERANCE FOR PAIN

Research shows that there is no such thing as a general pain tolerance. Some people just feel more pain than others. The duration or severity of pain can't be predicted. Simply put, you cannot be the judge of what hurts someone, or how long it should hurt.

The tolerance of pain is best defined as the *duration and intensity of pain that the person is willing to endure.* Pain tolerance, pain perception and the expression of pain are all unique to the individual. Furthermore a person's tolerance for pain varies from one situation to another. The person's emotional state, degree of fatigue, and the value or meaning of the pain for that patient all influence tolerance to pain.

Many care givers believe that the more experience a person has with pain, the more endurance and the greater tolerance they will develop. In fact, people who experience chronic pain usually have a *lower* tolerance combined with a higher level of anxiety because they know how severe the pain can be and how hard it may be to get relief.

ATTITUDES ABOUT PAIN

In America we have an unrealistic and stoic attitude about pain. Most of us feel that people should be able to cope with pain, and that to ask for help is a sign of weakness. This causes many care givers to underestimate the severity of pain in those who report it, and to adopt the attitude that the person should, "just learn to live with it."

This attitude also causes many people in pain to refuse medication that could help them because they don't want to appear to be "weak." I have had many people tell me they don't complain about pain because they want to be a "good patient" or they feel that a stoic response to pain or exhaustion somehow makes them a better person

As a clinical psychologist, I have never been a strong proponent of medication, but I think we are very wrong headed and ignorant about pain treatment in this country. Too many people suffer needlessly because of our negative attitudes about pain medication.

In addition, many physicians are reluctant to prescribe pain medication out of fear of repercussions from federal agencies, who also have this unrealistic attitude about medicating pain. A doctor who doles out pain medication liberally is often red-flagged, and called on the carpet for his or her "excessive" prescribing habits. This must change.

Another barrier to medicating pain is the unrealistic fear of addiction. Despite an abundance of evidence that narcotic drugs do not cause addiction in pain patients, many health care professionals persist in believing that addiction is a problem.

A survey of 1,781 nurses done in 1989 showed that 31 percent of them thought pain killing drugs should not be given because of potential addiction. Because of this mistaken belief, many health care professionals continue to refuse these drugs to those who need them. Others minimize the amount of pain medication a person can receive, making the therapy useless. These attitudes are archaic and harmful.

Effectively eliminating pain can do wonders for a person's quality of life. The priority for patients should always be comfort, not courage.

It has also been found that many chronic pain patients, including cancer patients, refuse to take opiate based pain medication because they believe that they would develop tolerance to the drugs, and therefore the drugs would become ineffective. In reality, opioid drugs have no "analgesic ceiling," that is, the level of these drugs can be increased to effective levels.

Finally, many health care workers underestimate the severity of the person's pain, and overestimate the effectiveness of the medication they are giving. If a person who has received pain medication a few hours before claims that they are still in pain, they are often told, "I'm sorry, you just got a pain pill. You'll have to wait two more hours." This is equivalent to telling the patient that you think they are lying.

PLACEBOS

A *placebo* is any treatment or medication that produces a response in a patient because of their belief that it will work, not because it has any actual therapeutic property. The problem with placebos is that people who respond positively to them may be wrongly perceived by care givers as malingering or fabricating their pain. This is seldom true. However, I have seen staff members give residents placebos because they think the person is lying about their pain, or because, "They don't know the difference."

The most common types of chronic pain

headache

low back

arthritis

muscle pain

dental pain

cancer pain

post operative

The use of placebos is never justified to determine the existence of pain. Since most people have some response to a placebo, no conclusion other than that the patient believes in the intent and efficacy of the treatment should be drawn from a placebo response. While placebos have a place in research trials, using them for diagnosis is unwise.

DEPRESSION

In the elderly, pain and depression may be closely linked—pain can be exacerbated by co-existing depression, while many who experience chronic pain often become depressed and anxious.

Studies show that up to 59 percent of patients requesting treatment for depression also complain of recurring pain, and conversely, 87 percent of patients coming to chronic pain clinics exhibit the symptoms of depression.

Even when a person denies being depressed, they may exhibit the symptoms. In fact, most people are unaware of the symptoms of depression, and do not realize that depression can worsen pain. Common symptoms of depression include sleep disturbances, early morning awakening, psychomotor retardation or agitation, anorexia and weight loss.

In some cases of unrecognized depression, complaints of pain may be the person's way of explaining her loss of interest in life, her low energy, poor concentration, and guilt. In cases where pain complaints are accompanied by the symptoms listed above, behavioral interventions can help. (For more on depression, see chapter 7 in this book.)

PAIN AND COGNITION

Several studies that have shown that chronic pain can cause cognitive problems. In fact, in one recent study, the central processing speed (the time it takes to think) in chronic pain patients was significantly slower than in head injury patients. Pain interferes with attention, con-centration, and endurance, and can preoccupy a person to the degree that they cannot think clearly.

PAIN AND ACTIVITY

Arthritis and muscle pain does not improve with rest. In fact rest can make the pain worse. Furthermore, a person loses one percent of his muscle mass for each day he remains inactive. Inactivity can lead to *disuse syndrome*, and may result in the person losing the ability to walk

PAIN ASSESSMENT

A pain assessment should include:

1. A complete medical and psychological history

2. A thorough physical examination

3. A complete neurological examination

4. A description of the pain's location

5. Conditions that make the pain worse or better

6. The effect of the pain on the person's mood and behavior.

7. A screening for cognitive impairment

8. A screening for depression

9. A vision and hearing examination to screen for sensory deprivation

10. A review of the persons's activities of daily living

11. A gait and balance assessment

12. Have the person measure their pain

A pain scale is an efficient and simple way to measure pain intensity. It consists of a horizontal line, with two end points labeled "no pain" or 0 and "worst pain ever," or 10. Ask the person to mark the line that corresponds to pain intensity.

13. Have the person describe their pain

Tools such as the McGill Pain Questionnaire provide information about the quality of the pain experienced.

Also get a feeling for how the patient responds to treatment and relates to care givers. This will help you to assess possible secondary gains. The probability of pain-related behaviors is higher in people who have difficulty establishing a trusting and secure relationship.

Chapter twelve

HEARING LOSS

It was a winter day in 1994, I was visiting a with a lovely 86 year old woman named Gina, living in a retirement home in the southern part of Orange County, California. It was the week before Christmas, and the facility was holding a Christmas party. The meeting hall was filled with the aroma of cakes and cookies, and the room danced with the sounds of holiday music, tinkling silverware, and casual conversation.

But Gina sat alone in her room.

I found this odd because I knew how much she loved the company of others. She had lost her husband two years before, had no family, and craved social stimulation.

When I asked her why she was not at the party, she told me some very important things. "I would love to be in that room," she said, "but you see, I am hard of hearing. People don't know it. They just think I'm ignoring them.. When somebody walks up and says hello and I don't hear them, they think I'm stuck up."

"But you have two hearing aids," I said.

Behavioral Objectives

At the end of this section readers will be able to

State the incidence of hearing loss in the older population

Describe the common causes of hearing loss

Explain the social and emotional consequences of impaired hearing

Communicate effectively with hearing impaired adults

"Sure," Gina said, "but you don't realize that when you wear a hearing aid in a crowded room, the noise is overwhelming. Everything gets amplified. All I hear is a jangled, jumbled roar. I can't tell the voices from the background noise. It's unpleasant and overwhelming.

So, I'm faced with a dilemma. I can go to the party and be blasted with noise, turn my hearing aid down and be accused of being stuck up or stupid, or stay in my room and be lonely. I love being with people, but I hate going to gatherings because people treat me like I'm retarded or something."

Since that time I've heard similar complaints by many elderly people. Sadly, rather than fix the problem, many cope with their loss by isolating, withdrawing, and sinking into loneliness and depression. To prevent this from happening, do the following:

INTERVENTIONS FOR HEARING LOSS

1. Explore methods of hearing improvement.

A significant portion of hearing impaired adults refuse to use hearing aids. Common explanations for this include complaints that the device does not work properly, that it is uncomfortable, and that the person does not know how to operate it correctly. Another complaint is that the hearing aid is ineffective in noisy environments, as it does not filter out unwanted sounds.

Others complain that they do not know how to put the device improperly, that they forget to put it in, or that they keep losing it.

In clinical settings such as hospitals and long term care facilities, amplifiers may be a better alternative ti a hearing aid. These devices are worn around the neck and are larger, making them harder to lose and easier to operate. In addition the person is able to adjust the volume to fit the environment, making them more user friendly.

2.Have the person's hearing checked regularly.

About 30 percent of adults age 65 through 70, and about 50 percent of those over age 70 suffer some degree of hearing loss. Hearing impairment ranges from having difficulty understanding words or hearing certain sounds to total deafness.

Because hearing loss is gradual, the person may not be aware that their hearing has changed. Instead, they feel that others are talking to quietly, or mumbling. Undetected hearing loss is often the beginning of social isolation, suspicion and paranoia. Hearing loss can be cased by viral infections, vascular disorders (such as heart conditions or stroke), head injuries, wax buildup, tumors, certain medications, and age- related changes in the ear. These factors should always be considered when making a diagnosis in an elderly person.

Conductive hearing loss involves the blocking of sounds that are carried from the ear drums (the *tympanic membranes*) to the inner-ear. This may be caused by ear wax in the ear canal, fluid in the middle ear, or abnormal bone growth or infection in the middle ear.

Sensorineural hearing loss involves damage to parts of the inner ear or auditory nerve, and often occurs in older people. An audiologist can make an accurate diagnosis.

3. Tell friends, family, and all care givers about the person's hearing loss.

Many people try to hide a hearing problem. They are self conscious and ashamed. They may refuse to have their hearing checked, and refuse to wear a hearing aid. Instead of admitting that they can't hear, they pretend to

Signs of hearing impairment

Words are difficult to understand.

Another person's speech sounds slurred

The person cannot hear when there is background noise.

Speech can be hard understand.

Certain sounds are overly loud or annoying.

Constant hissing or ringing in the ears

Certain voices cannot be heard

119

understand what is being said.

As a result, they fail to reply to others, which makes them appear rude, or they misunderstand others and make statements that make no sense. This makes them appear to be out of touch with reality. This behavior can frustrate other residents and staff members. Eventually, people begin to avoid talking to the hearing impaired person, because it's too frustrating. This leads to hurt feelings and isolation. For these reasons. It's important tat everyone know about the person's hearing problem.

4. Educate others about hearing loss.

Ask the person to tell people what it is that they can and can't hear. Have them inform others about the problems of noisy environments.

5. Make sure the person wears their hearing aids.

Many people refuse to wear their hearing aids because they are in denial about their problem, or their pride prevents them from using them. Others simply forget that they have hearing aids. A sign on their door or mirror stating, "put in your hearing aids," usually fixes this problem.

6. Don't allow people to use hearing loss as a tool for ignoring others.

My grandmother was hard of hearing for most of her adult life. Because of this, she would often fail to respond when she was asked a question. Even so, I noticed that she never, ever, failed to hear the words, "dinner's ready." People can use their hearing problem as an excuse for ignoring things they don't want to hear—a phenomenon called *"selective hearing."*

Chapter thirteen

VISION PROBLEMS

Although it affects many elderly people, visual impairment is often unrecognized and misunderstood. Visual impairment is also related to higher risk of death in older people.

In 2004 researchers found that more than 28 million Americans over age 40 have eye ailments serous enough to put them at risk for vision loss and blindness. This number is expected to soar as our population continues to age..

Cataracts are the leading cause of blindness worldwide, affecting an estimated 20.5 million American adults, and the number of cases is expected to reach 30.1 million in the next 20 years.

Macular degeneration, glaucoma and diabetic retino-pathy are also major causes of blindness and vision loss and are strongly linked with aging.

In the clinical population the numbers are higher. It's estimated that 30 to 50 percent of nursing home residents are visually impaired to the degree that it interferes with daily functioning, and it's estimated that over 90 percent

Behavioral Objectives

At the end of this section readers will be able to:

Recount the extent of vision loss in the older population

Describe the impact of vision loss

Name the common signs of visual problems

Create a safe environment for visually impaired adults

Signs of vision problems

Brushes against the wall while walking.

Consistently bumps into objects.

Has difficulty walking on irregular or bumpy surfaces.

Goes up and down stairs slowly and cautiously, even with no other physical limitations.

Has difficulty getting food onto a fork.

Has difficulty cutting food or serving self from a serving plate.

Spills food off the plate while eating.

Pours liquids over the top of the cup.

Knocks over liquids while reaching across the table for another item.

of people over 70 have some form of cataracts.

As well as having trouble seeing, people who experience vision loss also lose much of their independence, their ability to function, and their self-worth.

A person with a vision problem may have trouble doing even simple tasks, such as getting dressed. This often leads to feelings frustration and anxiety. Normal parts of the environment, such as staircases, can become dangerous, and are avoided. Bumping into furniture causes bruises and broken skin, while missing a chair results in a painful fall. Some people may even have trouble finding their rooms.

When vison fails, simple pleasures like reading a newspaper, magazine or book become impossible. Watching television or even having a conversation with a friend become more difficult, as the visual component of communication is lost.

Visual impairment is not only overlooked by others, but often goes unrecognized by the person suffering it. Because visual loss is often gradual, the person slowly adapts to it, without being aware that the visual world is fading.

As people age, two types of visual problems occur—reduced color discrimination and the inability to tolerate glare. Colors with short light waves—such as green, blue, and violet—are much more difficult to see than are red, orange, and yellow. All colors appear duller than once were. Pastels fade and become indistinguishable. Dark colors, which can blend into the shadows, are worst of all. Danger lurks where dark floors, doors and walls blend together.

Care givers should always be looking for signs of

vision loss. The behaviors in the box on this page list the most common indicators of vision problems. Elderly people who experience five or more of these signs and symptoms should get a thorough eye examination from an ophthalmologist. In many cases, surgical procedures, glasses, medications, and adaptive devices can correct or improve the person's vision.

Care givers can use a variety of techniques to better communicate with persons who are visually impaired.

BEHAVIORAL INTERVENTIONS FOR VISUAL IMPAIRMENT

1. When walking into the person's room, identify yourself and anyone else accompanying you.

Older adults with low vision often find it difficult to identify facial features, but they still recognize voices. Conversely, when leaving a room, announce that you are going. Otherwise the person may not realize that you have gone

2. Explain to the person exactly what you plan to do.

Tell them in advance if you are going to touch them, give them something, or take something away.

3. Avoid using the pronouns "he" or "she" when referring to someone in a group

Instead, identify each person by name. This will allow the visually impaired person to know who is present, and who is being talked about.

4. Always be sure to include the person in a conversation.

Signs of vision problems

Performing Daily Activities

Exhibits changes in reading, watching television, walking, or performing hobbies.

Squints or tilts the head to the side to get an object in focus.

Has difficulty identifying faces.

Has difficulty in locating familiar objects, even in a familiar environment.

Reaches out for objects in an uncertain manner.

Has difficulty identifying colors and selects clothing in unusual color combinations

Reading and Writing

Can't read mail or a newspaper.

Holds reading material close to the face or at an angle.

Writes less clearly end precisely and has difficulty writing on the line.

Finds lighting in the room inadequate for reading and other activities.

Visually impaired people are not able to pick up the subtle social cues that tell us when it is our turn to speak, so take special care to include them.

5. When speaking to a visually impaired person, always address them by name.

If they cannot see you, they may not be aware that you are speaking to them.

6. Don't automatically assume that the person would like to be helped.

Never force help on a person. Older adults with vision impairments are still able to do many things independently and might feel patronized by caregivers who offer too much assistance.

7. During personal care activities, allow the person to feel the items to be used.

Be sure to describe size shapes, and colors. Explain each task step-by-step. Encourage the person to complete a task independently, offering praise when appropriate.

8. Communicate with the person face-to-face and within close range.

This strategy allows the person to see you clearly, and read body language.

9. When offering seating, be sure to place the person's hand on the back or arm of the chair.

This allows then to orient themselves, and prevents accidents.

10. When leading a person who is visually impaired, have him hold your arm above the

elbow and follow a half a step behind you

Be precise when giving directions. For example, say, "There is a curb two feet away, directly to your left." When entering an unfamiliar setting, describe it in detail to the person, and point out such things as tables, chairs, and rugs.

11. Reduce glare

Soften glare from windows by using adjustable blinds, shades, and curtains. Glare from glossy paper during reading can be reduced by using an overlay of clear yellow plastic. This also makes the print on the page darker.

Avoid positioning yourself in the path of a bright light from a window or lamp, because the glare will prevent the person from seeing you properly.

12. Provide adequate lighting

Older adults with fading vision require two to three times more light than the general population in order to see properly. Put chairs near windows to take advantage of natural light. Light should be provided throughout a room with additional light from floor and table lamps near activity areas.

Provide the person with the ability to adjust the light in their room. Use three-way bulbs, high-low switches and dimmers. Gooseneck lamps and other adjustable lamps allow the person to focus the light where it is needed most. Use lamp shades of heavy, dark material to help concentrate light on an activity. Lights should be placed so that they shine on the task at hand.

13. Use night lights in bedrooms, hallways, and other dimly lit areas.

This will orient and guide the person, and will prevent falls.

14. Avoid sudden changes of light intensity.

Older eyes have difficulty making the adjustment to a sudden change from dark to light, and the person may actually experience a temporary vision loss.

15. Use Color Contrast

Colors that are too similar can blend together and become indistinguishable. For example, a person with poor vision may have difficulty seeing a white toilet or sink against a white wall or floor. Make doorsills, doorknobs, and door borders a contrasting color from walls. Make furniture contrast against walls, and accessories contrast against furniture. Use brightly colored vases and lamps to make furniture easier to locate.

Use contrasting colors for the tops and risers of steps. The handrail should contrast against the wall. See that there is adequate lighting throughout the stairwell.

In the bathroom, make the toilet seat contrast with the bathroom walls and floor. Put contrasting-colored tape around the edge of the toilet seat and sink if necessary.

Make toiletries brightly colored to promote visibility. Consider painting the walls in the bathroom a contrasting color to the floor.

In the tub room, drape a dark-colored bath mat over the side of the tub to promote visibility.

16. During meals, use light-colored dishes against dark-colored tablecloths

Clear glasses or dishes may not be visible.

17. Serve milk or other light colored liquids In a dark cup.

Conversely, serve coffee or other dark-colored liquids in a white cup. This allows the person to assess the level of the liquid in the cup.

18. Food should contrast against the plates.

Servings should vary in color. For instance, avoid placing white rice, white meat chicken, and cauliflower on the same plate.

19. Structure the environment

Familiarize all persons who have visual impairments with their environments.

Make sure doors open flush to the wall and push chairs and other objects out of traffic paths. Keep the placement of furnishings constant. See that chairs are pushed up tightly to tables and that cupboard and dresser drawers are not sticking out.

Keep closets consistently organized to help persons low vision more easily locate clothes. Color code dresser drawers with tape and make dividers in the drawers to help them identify items. Mark or label drawers so items can be returned to the same places.

Chapter fourteen

HALLUCINATIONS

An *hallucination* is an internally generated experience that is interpreted as external. Although most people don't admit to hallucinations, over half of us will experience them at sometime in our lives—the most common hallucination being hearing one's name called.

Hearing your name called, hearing voices, or other sounds are all *auditory hallucinations*. This type of hallucination is generally found in people suffering from schizophrenia, but is also found in several organic conditions, such as epilepsy, brain, tumors, or drug intoxication.

The most prevalent type of auditory hallucination is *running commentary*, which is the experience of hearing one or more voices commenting on and critiquing everything the person does. These hallucinations often are composed of thought fragments and endless loops of sentences, which may be repeated hundreds of times a day. Even when the person is able to recognize that the voices are hallucinations, this type of problem is truly maddening.

A *command hallucination* is the phenomenon of

Behavioral Objectives

At the end of this section readers will be able to:

Define the types of hallucinations

Discuss the causes of hallucinations

Recognize the effect of hallucinations on the well being of older people

Discriminate between psychotic and non-psychotic hallucinations hearing a voice compelling the person to do or not do a certain act. A person experiencing command halluc- inations may feel compelled to harm himself of others.

It's been found that some auditory hallucinations are cased by sub-vocalization, that is, the hallucinating person is actually speaking to himself without knowing it. In these cases, having the person stick out their tongue can actually stop the voices.

Visual hallucinations are less common than auditory, but can be very frightening. People with brain damage sometimes hallucinate snakes, spiders, and other un- savory creatures.

The *Charles Bonnet syndrome* (CBS) is a type of visual hallucination characterized by the lack of psy- chosis. In 1769 Charles Bonnet noticed that his grand- father was having visual hallucinations. But other than the hallucination, he showed no evidence of mental illness. Since that time, many cases of this type of hal- lucination have been reported.

Visual hallucinations have been reported in elderly patients with diffuse Lewy body disease. There is also a 3 per cent prevalence of visual hallucinations among patients with macular degeneration.

Seizures in the occipital lobe (the part of the brain that processes vision) and in the frontal lobes may cause visual hallucinations. Occipital seizures, however, rarely cause complex, fully formed hallucinations—instead the person usually sees flashes of light or colors, seen only in the half of the visual field on the opposite side of the seizure focus. Frontal lobe seizures, on the other hand, may cause complex, violent visual hallucinations, without an alteration in consciousness.

These hallucinations are sometimes caused by strokes. One of my patients described her experience in the hospital after suffering a stroke which affected her visual cortex.

> "I thought I was fine until the nurse came into see me. She had these horrible, huge, distorted eyes. I was feeling sorry for her until my husband walked in. To my horror, his right should-er was missing. This is when I realized some-thing was wrong with me."

Nursing consultant Dr. Kathleen Buckwalter has described a classic case of both visual and auditory hallucination caused by loss of vision, a phenomenon that she likens to phantom limb experiences, and which she calls *phantom hallucinations.*

> The nursing home staff had initially asked me to see Mrs. C. because of her "visual hallucin-ations." When I queried her about "seeing things." She described the following scene in vivid detail. The image would come and go unexpectedly, and had become more frequent as her eyesight became progressively worse.

> Over the past year it was almost always the same scene—a World War I French battle-ground where her former fiancee (who had been killed in the war) was stationed with his battalion. Mrs. C. described in exquisite detail the landscape (which she had never seen), the soldiers' khaki uniforms. and even noted how the horses' lips curled when they whinnied, as if to laugh at her for being so startled by the sight of the vision.

> "Can't you see them—the horses and men over there on the wall?" she would ask, "Oh, they seem so real to me."

> Although somewhat amazed by her vision, Mrs. C. was not particularly frightened or

troubled by it and clearly understood that she was the only person able to see it.

Olfactory hallucinations are hallucinated smells. The most common are smelling rotting flesh or something burning. This type of hallucination is rare but important, as it is often the first sign of a brain tumor.

Several years ago I was called to see an elderly gentleman who was living in a nursing home in Long Beach, California. The staff was concerned because he was spending hours each day with his ear pressed to the Pepsi machine. He was in fact, experiencing a *functional hallucination.*

A functional hallucination is the experience of hearing voices coming from machinery, running water, and other external sounds. Often the voices coming from these places make comments about the person, or gives them information. Functional hallucinations are quite common, but often go undiagnosed because they are not widely known.

Tactile hallucinations are the imagined experience of being touched, or of having something crawling on the skin. This type of hallucination sometimes occurs during a toxic reaction to amphetamines of other drugs. It also may be a sign of psychosis.

Another common type of hallucinations are *hallucinations of widowhood* and *bereavement.* People who have recently lost a loved one often see him in the house, hear his voice calling to them, or hear his footsteps in the hall. A great number of people have vivid dreams of the lost person coming into the bedroom at night to speak to them. It is important to inquire about these things when a resident has suffered a loss, because discussing them can relive a great deal of anxiety.

Oftentimes, in order to find out if a person is experiencing hallucinations, you must ask. But Dr. Steven Dubovsky, professor of psychiatry in medicine at the University of Colorado School of Medicine, points out that people are afraid of hallucinations, are reluctant to admit having them, and often deny them even when they are asked.

> A patient I saw recently, when I asked him if he had ever seen things or heard things, told me "Well no I don't"
>
> I said, "Well, are there ever any times when you think you might hear someone call your name?" His answer was, "Well, sure, that happens all the time, isn't that normal?" I said, "Do you ever hear the phone ringing when it's not?"And he said, "Yeah, but everybody has that happen."
>
> I asked, "Do you ever hear a high pitched sound or a buzzing sound or an odd sound of any kind?" and he said, "Well, sometimes, but that's just a ringing in my ears."
>
> "Does it ever sound like it might be a voice?" I asked. "Oh, sure, but every-one hears that."
>
> Then I asked him, "Do you ever notice movement out of the corner of your eye and then you look again and there is nothing there?"
>
> "Well sure," he replied.
>
> Does it ever look like anything that you think you might recognize?" The patient said, "You mean, like a bat?" I said, "What about a bat?"
>
> He said, "No, I don't see bats." and I said, "Well, what else don't you see?" He said, "Well, I don't see animals, and I don't see a dog lying in the road."
>
> I said, "Why don't you see these things?" and he said, "Well, If I payed attention to them I'd be

crazy."

As mentioned earlier, sensory deprivation can often lead to hallucinations. Residents who do not get enough environmental stimulation sometimes create their own by hallucinating. Helping them to be more socially active can correct this problem.

Chapter fifteen

DELUSIONS

Paranoid symptoms in the elderly are common. The clinical term for paranoia is *Delusional Disorder*. About half of elderly people with delusional disorders have an underlying brain disease, often a vascular disorder. Other patients may suffer from *late-onset psychosis* which includes delusions.

As sense organs deteriorate, some people develop a condition called *sensory paranoia*. For example, Impaired hearing may cause people to misinterpret what is said to them—to hear an innocent statement as an insult. Impaired vision may cause a person to misinterpret an innocuous movement as a threat, and prompt him to strike out in order to protect himself. But, there are other causes of delusional disorder.

As people age, they often begin to lose their feelings of power and control. A person who has had to accept daily care giving has given up much of his autonomy, and has become dependent on others for survival. As power is turned over to caregivers, feelings of helplessness and unimportance arise.

Behavioral Objectives

At the end of this section readers will be able to

Define the term delusional disorder

Decribe the symptoms of a delusional disorder

List several types of delusions

Work effectively with people suffering from delusions

135

Reacting to these intolerable feelings, some people begin to manufacture false beliefs. These beliefs center around reactions to this loss of independence. To maintain a sense of importance, the person may come to distrust and devalue his care givers.

Delusions often begin with misinterpretations of a single incident—a casual comment or an innocuous event is taken as a personal attack. As delusions become more fixed, however, the facts of the original incident become so changed and distorted that the original situation is unrecognizable. Soon the incident can develop into elaborate, rigid systems of ideas.

SYMPTOMS OF DELUSIONAL DISORDER

Below are the most common symptoms associated with delusional disorder. The person suffering from a paranoid condition may have some or all of them.

Suspiciousness

In the early stages, people may come to erroneous conclusions that can be corrected. This type of delusion is called an *over-valued idea*. A person with an over-valued idea may often be dissuaded by using reason and logic.

However, as delusions become more solidified, no amount of confrontation or logic is effective. At this stage a person may come to believe that all conversations pertain to him. He may believe that people on radio and television programs are talking about him or giving him secret information. Ordinary events, such as seeing others talking and laughing together, are misconstrued—every-one is talking about him. This process of hearing personal content in unrelated information is called *ideas of reference.*

Suspicions may focus on one person, a particular group, or everyone. The paranoid person may actively search for clues, no matter how farfetched, to confirm his suspicions, and ignore any evidence to the contrary.

Delusions of persecution

As cognitive functions deteriorate, people develop delusions based on their feelings of vulnerability. These delusions of being harmed or mistreated are called *delusions of persecution*. The most common delusion of this type is the belief that someone is stealing from them. He may also think that his food is poisoned, and that care givers and family members are conspiring against him. He may believe that his care givers want to kill him. Other common delusions include being cheated, or being spied upon, followed, or harassed by a secret group of people.

As the years go by, new people become included in the delusions as enemies, and the person's list of grievances may grow longer and become more complicated. This group of conspirators is known as a *paranoid psuedocommunity*.

Jealously and possessiveness

A person who is paranoid may become convinced that their mate is unfaithful. Seemingly insignificant situations become blown out of proportion and used to confirm this belief. The person will unceasingly accuse their mate of cheating on him, and may harass innocent people who he believes are the offending parties.

Paranoid people who accuse their mates of having illicit love affairs frequently tell them that they will stop questioning them if they will only "tell the truth."

Because of this, the spouses of paranoid people

sometimes actually confess to affairs they did not commit, only to discover that accusations increased rather than decreased.

Grandiosity

A common form of delusion is the *delusion of grandeur*. The person with this type of delusion amplifies his importance—he is no longer merely a person, he owns the hospital. He may believe that he is a powerful political figure, or royalty. In some instances he may believe he has been chosen by God for a special purpose, a condition called *paranoid illumination*.

The paranoid individual usually has an inflated view of his own abilities, believing he is all powerful or exceedingly brilliant. He may also believe that everyone else is incompetent, and act toward others in a rude and condescending manner.

Curiously, although many patients have delusions of grandeur, none of them actually leave the facility. It is as of part of them knows they need to taken care of.

BEHAVIORAL INTERVENTIONS FOR DELUSIONS

As previously mentioned, delusional persons often complain that people are stealing form them, of that their food is poisoned. All complaints by persons should be investigated, then sorted into realistic verses delusional. Realistic complaints should be dealt with, and the delusional one's modified therapeutically.

1. Find out what the person's idiosyncratic food preferences are.

Many paranoid people like their food from sealed cans, because they believe that sealed food could not have been poisoned by the staff.

2. Don't talk about the person in their presence or within their earshot. Don't engage have whispered conversations near them.

Paranoid people think every conversation is part of the conspiracy against them. Take precautions against rein-forcing this belief.

3. If you take an object from them, tell them why you are doing it and what you are going to do with the object.

4. Pay attention to the content of the delusions.

Determine what environmental, historical, or social factors may be contributing to the present problem.

5. Every time the person complains, have them fill out a complaint sheet.

This makes then feel that someone is recognizing and validating their complaints. It will also create a record of their complaints to which you can refer, and point out what was done. This keeps the person reality oriented. This also discourages them from making too many complaints, as filling out the from is work.

6. Discuss and encourage healthy activities and attitudes.

Reinforce any positive behavior, and point out constructive endeavors.

7. Don't dispute paranoid delusions.

People may be talked out of over-valued ideas, but not delusions. If you dispute the delusions, you will be seen as the enemy.

8. When the person begins to talk about paranoid material, remain calm and friendly.

Don't agree with statements that are false or actions that may be harmful to himself and others. If he trusts you and is not too set in his delusions, you may be able to express a different view. However, when doing this results in the person becoming angry, stop. Redirect the conversation to a neutral subject. You may also refocus the person by involving him in some activity or interest.

9. Limit the time that you spend talking about his paranoid complaints.

Convey to the person that you care, but that it is not productive for the two of you to talk endlessly about his problem.

10. Talk to the person in a clear, straightforward manner.

Paranoid people are mistrustful and look for hidden meanings. When you must obtain information, ask direct questions and offer reasons why you need to know.

11. Always keep your word.

Paranoid people are extremely sensitive to dishonesty. Do what you say you are going to do, and you will keep their respect.

12. Avoid surprises and un announced changes.

Most paranoid people are rigid by nature and need a structured, predictable environment. Surprises, even pleasant ones, may create confusion and hostile behavior.

13. Encourage the person to follow through with treatment.

If he is upset about some aspect of it, suggest that he discuss it with his doctor or therapist. The paranoid person may respond more favorably to someone he perceives as an authority figure.

14. Don't force control. Instead use persuasion to get the person to do things.

People who need daily care have little control in their lives. They will see forced control as part of a conspiracy to take away their power. If the person perceives that you are ordering him to do something, he will prepare for battle. Help the person see the practical advantage of what you asking him to do. Offer evidence that the change will be to his benefit. If he becomes angry or misunderstands why he should change, stop and try again later.

15. Don't tease or make jokes about paranoid people.

People suffering from paranoia have no sense of humor. They view these things as demeaning, and will react with hostility.

16. Do not react to sarcasm, irritability, accusations and blame.

Staff should not take accusations personally. Most paranoid people think that the staff is stealing from them. Recognize that a paranoid individual's remarks and behaviors are not actually related to you, but are due their disorder.

17. Beware of the paranoid that keeps written records of everything, has an enemies

Hypochondriasis & Depression

Depression

Patients claim to have great suffering from their symptoms.

Hostility is directed inward.

Social withdrawal is prominent and often dysfunctional.

Will discuss feelings and social life with minimal coaxing.

Episodes of somatic difficulties less frequent in mid-life.

Condition is cyclic over time.

Tolerate the side effects of antidepressants

Suicidal thoughts are common.

Hypochondriasis

Despite numerous reported symptoms, the person does not appear to be suffering significantly

Hostility is directed outward.

Social interaction is frequently decreased but not dysfunctional.

Insist on discussing their physical ailments to the exclusion of intrapersonal and interpersonal issues.

Frequent episodes of somatic difficulties in mid-life.

Condition tends to be consistent over time.

Do not tolerate the side effects antidepressants.

Suicidal thoughts are rare.

list, or stockpiles weapons.

These are the cardinal traits of the type of dangerous paranoid who will kill his perceived enemies. This type of person also may have a history of calling the police on neighbors, and filing lawsuits about perceived transgressions.

Chapter Sixteen

STROKES

A *stroke* is the destruction of brain cells caused by an interruption of blood flow to the brain. Strokes are the leading source of adult disability, and the number three cause of death (after heart disease and cancer). They afflict about 500,000 Americans each year.

Eighty percent of stroke victims survive, but they often suffer permanent loss of function, such as the loss of the ability to speak (called *aphasia*) or paralysis of part of the body. Strokes are also called *cerebral vascular accidents* (CVAs) but they are, in fact, not accidents; to a great degree, they can be predicted and prevented.

The number of strokes in the United States has decreased almost 50 percent in the last thirty years. This is attributed primarily to advances in the medical control of high blood pressure. Even so, over two million people a year suffer from strokes.

Researchers have found that a brain chemical called *calpain* may cause brain cell damage after a stroke. Normally calpain cleans up blocked receptors in neurons

Behavioral Objectives

At the end of this section readers will be able to

Describe the major types of strokes

Discuss the problems associated with brain damage

Discriminate between signs of left vs right hemisphere strokes

Recognized post-stroke depression

and facilitates memory transfer, but too much calpain in the system kills neurons.

When a stroke occurs, it is also followed by the release of glutamate, a chemical that causes brain damage. This phenomenon is called a *glutamate cascade.*

Strokes occur in three major ways. *Plaque* is the debris that blocks arteries in atherosclerosis. A blood clot that completely clogs an artery and causes a stroke is called a *thrombus,* and the incident is called a *thrombic stroke.* About 80percent of strokes are of the thrombic type. When a bit of plaque, called an *embolus* breaks off and clogs a smaller vessel or capillary, it is called an *embolic stroke.*

When an artery in the brain actually bursts, and blood spills into the brain, the incident is called a *hemorrhagic stroke.* This type of stroke usually occurs from a combination of atherosclerosis and high blood pressure. About 10 percent of strokes are of his type.

THE ARTERIES

The blood vessels that supply oxygen to the body are called *arteries.* The wall of an artery consists of several layers of smooth muscle. Blood is supplied to the human brain by four major arteries. The two *internal carotid arteries* supply about 85percent of total blood flow to t percent brain. The *vertebral arteries* supply the remaining 15 percent. If these vessels become blocked or clogged with plaque, blood flow to the brain is diminished, and this condition must be corrected to restore proper brain nourishment.

THE CAROTID ARTERIES

Two large arteries, called the *carotid arteries,* supply blood to the cerebral hemispheres. There is one carotid on each side of the neck.

A small branch of the carotid supplies blood to the artery of the eye. If this branch of the carotid artery becomes narrowed by atherosclerosis, and part of the plaque breaks off and travels to the brain, the afflicted person may experience a temporary loss of vision to one eye. People who have experienced this describe it as having a curtain drawn in front of their eye. These episodes may occur several times a day.

People over 40, particularly if they have diabetes or high blood pressure, should have their carotid arteries checked regularly. If narrowing of the carotid artery has occurred, a murmur (called a *bruit*) can be heard through a stethoscope. More sophisticated testing includes X rays with the use of dye, and computer analysis. The most recent technique for diagnosing carotid narrowing is sonar examination.

Blockage of the carotids is serious. If the carotid artery becomes so blocked that blood flow to the brain is impaired, surgery may be required. The operation, called an *endarterectomy*, is similar to roto-rootering the artery. If the damage to the artery is severe, doctors may replace a portion of it with a vessel from another part of the body, often from the leg.

Many doctors believe that neurological deficits and cognitive functioning improve after the procedure, because of improved blood flow to areas of the brain which were impaired before the operation. If the blockage is not too severe, aspirin can sometimes be used as a substitute for this surgery, because it impedes the formation of blood clots. Keep in mind, however, that aspirin can cause other problems, such as internal bleeding and confusion.

THE BASILAR ARTERY

At the base of the brain is the *basilar artery*. This artery furnishes the brain stem and the merging cranial nerves with blood.

Patients with atherosclerosis in the basilar artery often complain of vertigo and nausea. Vertigo is the very unpleasant feeling of spinning around in space. Often the person has the feeling that everything around him is spinning uncontrollably. This feeling can be very uncomfortable, and can sometimes cause vomiting.

Patients with blockage in the basilar artery frequently complain of having tingling sensations around their mouth, and may have difficulty pronouncing words. They may also have swallowing problems.

When the blood flow through this artery is interrupted, the person may suffer a brief loss of consciousness, or may fall down. There may also be a loss of equilibrium, staggering, and behavior that mimics drunkenness. Some people with this problem are not able to walk at all.

Many of these symptoms can also be caused by an infection of the inner ear, and should not be confused with basilar artery problems. Also, a rare congenital disorder called *Arnold-Chiari's malformation* has been known to cause similar symptoms. These things should be ruled out before basilar artery damage is considered.

TRANSIENT ISCHEMIC ATTACKS

Tiny strokes, called *transient ischemic attacks* (TIAs), mimic strokes in their symptoms, causing numbness, nausea and dizziness. But unlike actual strokes, which can cause permanent disability, TIAs last only up to 24 hours. TIAs are caused by a temporary decrease in the blood flow to different parts of the brain. When this occurs, there's often a loss of motor ability and thinking capacity that lasts several minutes to a day, and then disappears.

The major cause of TIAs is atherosclerosis of the arteries supplying the brain. Other less common causes include episodes of irregular heartbeats, low blood pressure and brain tumors.

If the blood flow to a part of the brain called the hippocampus is blocked during a TIA, memory loss will occur. Repeated episodes of TIAs over time may cause dementia. Other symptoms of TIAs include brief flashes of numbness in the face and the arms, or sudden weakness of an arm or a leg with the inability to move.

Having a TIA can be a terrifying experience, but soon after the episode, the person feels fine. For this reason, people often fail to seek help, or may even neglect to tell anyone about the episode.

Even though people with TIAs may have no signs of heart disease, they should have a thorough cardiac workup, because many also have hardening in the arteries of the heart. In fact, the cause of death in people with TIAs is usually heart attack.

In 1978, the Mayo Clinic reported that one-third of patients with TIAs will suffer a stroke within five years of the first attack. Twenty per-cent will suffer stroke within one month of the initial attack, and 50percent within a year. As we shall see, strokes can be devastating and sometimes fatal events. But they are, in part, preventable.

In the past few years, it's been discovered that injections of a clot-dissolving drug called *tissue plas-*

Medical conditions that can be mistaken for stroke

Multiple sclerosis

Vertigo

Inner ear problems

Migraines

Seizures

Tumors

Hematomas

minogen activator (TPA) can dramatically improve the chances of stroke patients recovering with few lasting effects. In a study of 624 stroke patients, victims were randomly assigned to get either TPA or a placebo. After three months, doctors judged the patients' conditions on four scales of stroke symptoms. Depending on the measure used, those getting TPA were between 30 to 50 percent more likely to have full or nearly complete recoveries.

On the most conservative of these scales, the doctors found that 31 percent of the patients receiving TPA showed no permanent disability, or were left with minor symptoms such as slight weakness in one arm. By comparison, only 20 percent of those in the untreated group were this fortunate.

To be effective, TPA must be administered within the first three hours of the onset of symptoms. This means that caregivers have to be well educated in recognizing the symptoms of stroke, and quick to make an emergency call when one occurs. Since prompt treatment is essential, strokes are know considered emergencies by ambulance crews and hospitals.

Before a person is given TPA, he must be given a CAT scan first to make sure that the stroke is from a blood clot in the brain and not from a broken blood vessel.

In addition giving TPA too late in the course of a stroke may trigger bleeding in the brain, causing further damage. In a major study in which European doctors gave TPA to patients six hours after stroke symptoms began, the drug increased the risk of death by two-thirds.

Even when the drug is used properly, it increases bleeding in the brain in 6 percent of patients. However, the study concludes that this hazard is offset by the reduction in symptoms among stroke survivors. When given to the right person at the right time, it can prevent lifelong disability.

BEHAVIORAL PROBLEMS RESULTING FROM STROKE

People with right hemisphere strokes may exhibit a syndrome called *neglect*. People with this condition are not aware of things that occur on the left side of their body. Although they may lose function in the entire left half of their body, some seem completely unaware that anything is wrong, a condition known as *anosagnosia*. In fact, some victims exhibit a condition called *somato-phrenia*—they do not even recognize their own arm or leg as theirs. If you ask them about the arm, they may say, "Yes I see that arm, but it's not mine." In rare cases, the person may even come to hate the useless limb, a condition which is known as *misoplegia*.

In addition to being disconcerting, these conditions can be dangerous, because the afflicted person, being unaware that they are paralyzed, may attempt to stand, walk, or engage in other behaviors that can case them harm.

In addition some right-brain stroke victims may exhibit a condition known as *Capgras Syndrome*. People with this disorder believe that their family members and friends have been replaced with exact duplicates. They usually believe that these imposters are involved in some conspiracy—often a plot to steal their money.

Because language is located in the left side of the brain in most people, people with left hemisphere strokes often lose their ability to speak, a condition called *expressive aphasia*.

Symptoms of a right-hemisphere stroke

Left side paralysis or weakness

Impulsive behavior

Difficulty performing daily tasks

Problems with perception

Left side neglect

Problems with visual memory

Incessant talking

Poor judgement

Short attention span

Time disorientation

Loss of the left visual field

Impairment in abstract thinking

Emotional outbursts

Lethargy

Symptoms of a left-hemisphere stroke

Paralysis or weakness on the right side of the body

Partial or complete loss of understanding language

Partial or complete loss of the ability to speak

Impaired attention

Impaired thought processing

Decreased problem-solving ability

Poor judgment

Poor insight

Impaired voluntary movements

Confusion between left and right

Lack of insight

Loss of the right visual field

Memory problems

Low tolerance for frustration

Impulsive behavior

Slowness

Depression

But even though the person may lose language function, they may still be able to sing. It seems that songs are a right hemisphere task. Because of this, it is possible in some cases to teach people who cannot speak to *sing* their requests.

POST-STROKE DEPRESSION

It is normal for stoke victims to go through a bout of depression and mourning. For those with permanent losses of function, the losses must be grieved.

The treatment for post stroke depression is the same for any depression and is discussed in chapter seven of this book.

DEMENTIA AND STROKE

There is some evidence that stroke victims are at higher risk for dementia. This makes sense, in that they have already suffered brain damage. In addition, the fact that they had the stroke means that they already suffer from high blood pressure, heart disease, or arteriosclerosis—all of which are contributing factors to dementia.

Section three

MANAGING BEHAVIOR PROBLEMS

Care giving Activities Rated by the Elderly and their Nurses

Statement	Elders' Rank	Nurses' Rank
See that the bed pan or urinal are provided when needed	1	11
Relieve my anxiety by explaining reasons for my symptoms	2	23
Notice when I am in pain and give me medications if ordered	3	3
Observe the effects of treatments ordered by the physician	4	5
Give prescribed medications on time	5	17
Carry out doctor's orders	6	10
Help me to assume a comfortable or appropriate position	7	15
Encourage me to take more responsibility for my own care while in the hospital	8	31
Check on bowel functioning and report problems to the doctor	9	12
Make me feel you are happy to care for me	10	25
Take time to listen to me	11	7
Notice changes in my condition and report them	12	1
Provide me with a clean, comfortable bed	13	37
Provide a comfortable, pleasant environment (proper temperature, free from odors and disturbing noises)	14	40
Teach me about the medications that I will be taking at home	15	6
Take my temperature and pulse	16	21
See that my food is served properly	17	41
Give me pamphlets to read and/or talk with me about my illness in order to help me understand how to care for myself	18	28
See that the unit is clean and tidy	19	48
Provide privacy during my bath and treatments	20	16
Be sure that I have necessary equipment—glass, towel, soap, blanket, etc.	21	38
Help me maintain or restore normal elimination	22	9
Take special care of my skin so it does not become sore	23	2
Help me in and out of bed	24	27
Discuss with me the amount and type of activity I should have at home	25	39
Help me understand how to plan the diet I will need at home	26	32
Assist me with meals	27	18
Be understanding when I am irritable and demanding	28	30
Help me get necessary exercise while I am in the hospital	29	35
Be sure I have a copy of my diet	30	43
Arrange for a public health nurse to visit me at home	31	26
Explain about diagnostic tests ahead of time so that I will know what to expect	32	8
Give or assist me with a daily bath	33	42
See that I have food and/or fluids between meals	34	33
Ask the dietician to serve me soft foods that I am able to chew	35	24
Make me comfortable by rubbing my back	36	44
Allow me to make decisions about my care	37	20
Plan my care so that I will be able to rest while in the hospital	38	36
Tell my doctor that I am worried about my condition	39	29
Change my position frequently	40	13
Consider my personal preferences when caring for me	41	22
Take time to talk with my family and answer their questions	42	19
Help me make arrangement for my care at home	43	14
Talk with my family about my illness and the care I will need at home	44	4
Help me with grooming, such as care of my nails, hair, end/or shaving	45	49
Arrange for my priest, minister, or rabbi to visit me	46	45
Assist me with care of my mouth and teeth	47	34
Talk with me about topics unrelated to my illness, such os news, hobbies, other interests	48	47
Make it possible for me to observe my religious practices in the hospital	49	46
Plan some diversion or recreation for me	50	50

Adapted from Hudson & Sexton: Perceptions about Nursing Care *Journal of Gerontological Nursing* Dec 1996 22(12):41-46

Chapter seventeen

BEHAVIOR PROBLEMS

In 1987, in order to establish higher health care quality standards for the long-term care industry, the federal government implemented federal nursing home legislation known as the Omnibus Budget Reconciliation Act (OBRA).

The intent of this legislation was to create a legal means for eliminating substandard and poorly managed facilities, to upgrade marginal facilities, and to bring all facilities into compliance with the newly mandated levels of quality care. In short, they wanted the residents to get better treatment.

The method of enforcement of this legislation has been frequent observation of the facilities, followed by severe sanctions for non-compliance. In fact, the failure to meet the standards of quality care can result in every person connected with a facility facing civil and criminal liability.

The new OBRA guidelines became law in 1990, one of which was that every care facility be required to

Behavioral Objectives

At the end of this section readers will be able to

Understand the purpose of treatment guidelines

List the common behavioral problems found in older adults

Name the goals of OBRA guidelines

Discuss the reasons that behavioral interventions should precede medical interventions develop a Quality Assurance Plan and quality assurance procedures.

The new health care standards are enforced by periodic surveys, which has been a major source of anxiety and frustration, because many long term care facility owners believe that the fulfilling of these require-ments greatly increases the cost of long-term health care.

However, in reality, better care means less problems, less paperwork, more customer and staff satisfaction, and an improved public image. Taking better care of the people you care for has no down-side. In addition, surveys show that the quality of care has significantly improved since the legislation went into effect.

The OBRA Guidelines are designed to:

1. Minimize environmental stressors, including room noises, facility disarray, staff and roommate problems.

2. Minimize psychosocial stressors, such as family and loss issues.

3. Eliminate behavioral problems caused by medications and illness.

4. Decrease the use of psychotropic medications, using them only in instances when behavioral interventions have proven unsuccessful.

OBRA requires that a patient who is having problems be assessed, diagnosed, and treated via an inter-disciplinary treatment plan. The goal of the treatment program is to obtain quality care for all emotional and behavioral problems. This treatment program usually begins with behavioral and psycho-therapeutic treatment, as well as interpersonal and social intervention.

Psychotropic medication is to be used only after all other avenues of intervention have been explored. This means that every facility have a clearly delineated plan of psychological and behavioral intervention for all emotional and behavioral problems. Medications are deemed appropriate only in cases of Major psychosis, Hunting-ton's disease, Tourette's syndrome, for people with dementia who are experiencing psychotic symp-toms, and for short term amelioration of problems such as nausea and intractable hiccuping.

BEHAVIORAL PROBLEMS

Research shows that about three fourths of the people in retirement, assisted living, or long-term care facilities will exhibit problem behaviors at some time. These behaviors can be damaging to the person and to others, may interfere with care, and may upset other residents, the resident's family, and stress the care giving staff. These problem behaviors add to the already heavy work-load of the care givers.

Many problems in the elderly originate from per-ceived lack of caring from the staff and other caregivers. This is caused in part by the differing perceptions about what is important to patients. On page 134 are the results of an interesting and valuable study which showed clearly that caregiver's may misunderstand the needs of their clients. I encourage you to examine this table carefully.

Although the elderly present with a multitude of

Abusive behavior
Agitation
Anger
Arguing
Anxiety
Attention Seeking
Biting
Combativeness
Complaining
Crying
Cursing
Delirium
Depression
Disorientation
Delusions
Difficulty dressing
Eating problems
Entering other's rooms
Fighting
Grabbing
Hallucinations
Hitting
Hopelessness
Impulse control
Isolation
Manipulation
Medication compliance
Memory problems
Moaning
Muttering
Pacing
Paranoia
Psychosis
Resisting care
Rummaging
Screaming
Sleep problems
Spitting
Sexual inappropriateness
Undressing
Unsafe movement
Wandering
Yelling

behavioral problems, the most common are listed in the margin of this page.

In the past, many of these problems were dealt with through psychotropic medication, seclusion, and restraints. The problem was that these methods usually didn't work, and they often did little more than prevent the resident from engaging in the problem behavior. In addition, many of the medications used for these problems had undesirable side effects, and some actually made the symptoms worse.

However, research revealed that a great many of these problems could be more effectively corrected through the use of psychotherapy and behavioral intervention. These findings led to the new guidelines now used for the care of the elderly.

As mentioned earlier, emotional and behavior problems occur in the elderly for the same reasons they occur in anyone—from stress, grief, and lack of coping skills. The major difference in working with the elderly is the possible contribution to these problems from two other major factors—medical problems and cognitive impairment. Once these have been assessed, intervention can proceed.

Chapter eighteen

ASSESSMENTS

Assessments should always be done before treatment begins. The family, a physician, or the previous facility will generally provide some assessments, historical information, and the rationale for treatment.

Begin as soon as possible to identify the causes of any apparent emotional or behavioral problems. If the problems are those that are normally treated by the staff, then treatment should begin immediately. If the presenting problems indicate that additional psychiatric or medical assessment is needed, notify the primary care physician who can order further consultations, lab tests and psychological testing.

If it appears that the symptoms are not the result of a medical problem, but are caused by psychosocial stressors or environmental factors, a behavioral assessment should be done.

BEHAVIORAL ASSESSMENT

A complete behavioral assessment is the first step in any effective intervention. Behavioral assessments

Behavioral Objectives

At the end of this section readers will be able to

Describe the value of a complete assessment

List the components of defining the causes of problem behaviors

Perform a brief cognitive assessment

Assess higher cognitive functioning

Medical Assessment for Behavioral Symptoms

Vital Signs:

temperature
blood pressure,
    standing and lying
    down, both arms
respiratory rate
pulse rate,
blood glucose
cognitive status
orientation.

Review Medications:

medications added
medications stopped
dose changes
change in routes of
    administration

Review the Chart for:

change in urination
change in bowel habits.
change in food intake
change in fluid intake
change in sleep patterns
falls or injuries
changes in orientation

General Body presentation:

guarding or protecting any
    part of body
neurologic problems
asymmetries or swellings

Range of Motion:

limitations
tenderness or pain
fractures

should begin by asking the questions:

What are the presenting problems?

What could be causing them?

What can be done to remedy them?

Behavioral assessments contain the following steps:

1. Identify all of the problem behaviors.

Clearly define each target behavior.

2. Observe the behavior for several days if possible, and record when, where, and how often it occurs.

3. Log the severity of the behavior.

4. Identify the causes or antecedents to the behavior.

Is there any medical condition that could cause this behavior? Could it be a medication problem? Have there been any recent environmental changes? What was happening right before the problem began? Can the behavior be tied to any external trigger?

5. Log the consequences of the behavior.

What happens after the behavior occurs? How is the patient being rewarded for the behavior?

6. Look for any medical conditions or medications that could be causing the problem.

This is an absolute must. Without a thorough screening for these conditions, all behavioral intervention will be ineffective.

7. Assess the person's level of cognitive

functioning.

What portion of the behavior could be caused by dementia, what portion could be from a pre-existing personality trait? What portion could be responsive to psychotherapy or behavior management?

This assessment is usually done by conducting a complete *mental status examination*, which includes assessment of orientation, thinking, memory, judgement, and insight. (An example of a mental status exam appears in the next section of this chapter.)

8. Is the person aware of the behavior?

Determine if the person is aware that they are engaging in a problem behavior.

9. Assess the meaning of the behavior.

Does the person do the behavior for a specific reason? Is he able to tell you the reason?

10. Is the behavior reality based?

Ask the resident why they are doing the behavior. Behaviors based on delusions or psychosis are handled differently than reality-based behavior.

MENTAL STATUS EXAM

The mental status examination is a global assessment of the person's level of functioning that will allow yo to match your interventions to the person's ability. Most mental status exams contain the following elements:

APPEARANCE & LEVEL OF FUNCTIONING:

The first step is to get a picture of the person's overall appearance. Observe the following:

1. Is the person clean and neat, or sloppy in

Medical Assessment for Behavioral Symptoms

Abdomen:

  distention.
  enlarged bladder.
  catheter problems.

Skin:

  redness
  swelling.
  bruises

Check Restraints

Environmental Changes:

  room change
  new roommate
  remodeling
  furniture moved or replaced

Recent Social Changes.

  family visits
  personal loss
  activity schedule

Signs of Depression.
  sadness
  crying
  anxiety
  irritability
  apathy
  feelings of worthlessness
  withdrawn
  physical complaints

Sleep problems:

insomnia
sleeping too much
change in sleep pattern
fatigue
decreased energy

Assessment of function

1. Reality testing
   Distinction between inner and outer
   Accuracy of perceptions

2. Insight
   Reflective awareness
   Discrepancy between actual competence and sense of competence?

3. Judgment
   Awareness of logical consequences
   Evidence of this awareness in behavior
   Emotional appropriateness

4. Sense of reality
   Extent of derealization
   Extent of depersonalization

5. Sense of self
   Self-identify
   Self-esteem
   Clarity of boundaries

6. Impulse Control
   Control of drives and emotions
   Ability to delay impulses

7. Degree and kind of relatedness
   Narcissistic
   Symbiotic
   Degree to which others are perceived independently of oneself
   Object constancy

8. Thought
   Memory
      Immediate
      Delayed
      Remote
   Concentration
   Attention
   Ability to conceptualize
   Primary process
   Ability to process & synthesize information

9. Defensive functioning
   Weakness or obtrusiveness of defenses

10. Stimulus barrier
    Threshold for stimuli
    Management of excessive input

11. Autonomy

appearance?

Poor hygiene can be a sign of dementia, depression, or psychosis.

2. Do they appear older than their stated age?

Physical deterioration is often accompanied by mental deterioration.

3. Is the person able to sit still?

Restlessness can be a sign of dementia, anxiety or mania.

4. Does she exhibit any involuntary movements?

Unusual or involuntary movements may be a sign of tardive dyskinesia.

5. Is there any evidence of paralysis or any other restriction of movement?

Paralysis is most often caused by stroke, and may be accompanied by depression or cognitive problems.

6. Are there any abnormalities of speech?

Loss of articulation, that is slurring of speech or inability to pronounce words, usually indicates loss of brain function. *Pressured speech*, a rapid unending stream of talking, is indicative of *mania. Tangential speech*, where ideas ramble and the focus is missing, is a sign of *psychosis. Profanity, yelling*, and *verbal abuse* are often signs of dementia.

7. I there any evidence of visual or hearing impairment?

Establishing the person's ability to see, hear, and

respond to outer stimuli will help you determine her ability to respond to the rest of the assessment

ORIENTATION:

Establish the person's awareness of the environment by asking:

1. Were are we?

2. What year is this?

3. What state are we in?

4. What is today's date?

5. Ask the person to tell you where they have been for the past twenty-four hours, and what they did there.

Asking "Can you tell me where you are?" will give you two pieces of information. First, if the person does not know where he is, you need to check for further evidence of disorientation. Second, if the answer this question by saying, "Yes," you need to check for dementia—people with cognitive impairment often answer questions very concretely.

PERSONAL INFORMATION:

These questions will give you information about the person's history, level of education, and remote memory function.

1. What year were you born?

2. Where were you born?

3. How old are you?

4. How much schooling do you have?

5. What did you do for a living?

6. How many children do you have?

An inability to precisely answer these types of questions indicates a profound loss of intellectual ability.

GENERAL INFORMATION:

Ask the following:

1. Who is the president of the United States?

2. Who was President before him?

3. How many states are there?

4. Where to you keep your money?

5. Please count backwards from 30 to 1.

These questions give you a feel for the person's general fund of knowledge and remote memory function.

SPEECH AND LANGUAGE:

This segment of the assessment evaluates the speech centers of the brain.

1. Have the person say, "No ifs, ands, or buts."

People who cannot pronounce this sentence correctly may have brain damage to the speech centers of the brain.

2. Have the person read a sentence aloud. Then have her write out the sentence word for word from memory.

This gives you an idea of how well the person can read, whether they can comprehend and retain what they read, and how well they can write.

3. Name three objects such as a pen, watch

and a ring, and ask the person to name the objects without pausing.

Inability to name common objects is a strong sign of dementia.

4. Ask the person to name all of the cities, colors, and animals they can, each category within one minute.

Inability to do this is indicative of dementia. People who cannot do this will often confabulate.

> The best answer I ever got to the request to name ten animals was, "A crane and nine loons." Another woman told me, "Sarah Johnson." When I said I thought Sarah Johnson didn't count as an animal, she told me, "Oh yeah? I guess you don't know her."

5. Ask the subject to spell the word *world* backward.

People with even minimal brain problems cannot do this because it requires the use of higher brain functions in the language hemisphere that are easily disrupted.

MOTOR FUNCTIONS:

1. Ask the person to put her right hand on her left ear.

People with severe abnormalities in the language center of the brain often cannot do crossover tasks. Deep lesions in the midbrain structures can produce a similar syndrome.

2. Ask the person to complete simple tasks, such as combing his hair and tying his shoes.

If he can't do these things, he has *apraxia*, the

Factors in the Assessment of Activities of Daily Living (ADL)

1. Bathing
2. Eating
3. Dressing
4. Combing hair
5. Brushing teeth
6. Urinating
7. Defecating
8. Speaking
9. Writing
10. Seeing
11. Typing
12. Hearing
13. Grasping
14. Lifting
15. Tactile discrimination
16. Climbing stairs
17. Walking
18. Sitting
19. Standing
20. Lying down
21. Driving
22. Flying
23. Riding
24. Sexual function
25. Participation in usual sexual activity

inability to perform meaningful skilled movements. This may involve abnormalities of both language and motor parts of the brain.

HIGHER BRAIN FUNCTIONS:

To test the function of the frontal lobe, a part of the brain that controls executive functions, give the following test of hand movements.

1. Ask the person to make a fist and to use her fist to strike a table or armrest with one hand.

2. Ask her to open her hand and hit the table or armrest with the open palm of the other hand.

3. Ask her to alternate between using her fist with one hand and palm with the other ten times in rapid succession.

4. Ask her to reverse the hands.

If she makes a mistake the first time, have her try again. Failing both times is a sign of cognitive impairment.

5. Ask the person to subtract 7 from 100.

6. Ask, "What is 12 X 13?"

To do this problem, the person must be able to manipulate numbers in her mind.

PROVERB INTERPRETATION

1. Ask the person the meaning of,

"A rolling stone gathers no moss."

"People who live in glass houses shouldn't throw stones."

People with the beginning stages of cognitive damage will often interpret the proverbs literally, for example, "If you throw stones at a glass house you'll break the glass."

CLOCK TEST

Have the person draw the face of a clock, and put the hands on ten-minutes-after-four. Assess the person's ability to comprehend and execute this task. If all the numbers have been put on one side, for example, indicates *neglect*. The inability to put the hands in the proper place suggests mental impairment.

FIGURE DRAWING

1. Have the person copy or reproduce drawings of increasing complexity.

For example, give the person a sheet of paper that has drawings of simple shapes on the left side and ask them to copy the shapes on the right-hand side of the page. Grade the person's drawings for accuracy.

2. Ask the subject to draw a three-dimensional picture of a house.

LONG-TERM MEMORY

Tell the person three unrelated words and ask him to recall the words, in their exact order, immediately, and at the end of four minutes.

During the four minute interval, have them do a few math problems. People with normal memory function usually get three out of three. Two out of three is acceptable. Inability to recall the words indicates processing and memory problems.

INSIGHT

The data gathered thus far should give you a good idea about the person's thought processes, ability to think, and memory function.

1. Ask the person, "Do you have any problems with memory or thinking?"

If their answer does not fit your findings, the person has impaired insight. People with moderate memory problems will usually be aware that they are having trouble, while people with severe problems will usually tell you their memory is fine.

JUDGEMENT

1. Ask the person what they would do if they broke a friend's favorite vase.

Ask him what he could do to prevent the person from becoming angry. The answer will give you information about the person's sense of judgement and coping skills.

SOCIAL APPROPRIATENESS

1. Ask the person what behaviors are appropriate for certain social situations.

For example, what would he do if he saw a person drop their wallet? A person who cannot give a socially appropriate answer to this type of question displays impaired judgement.

The information you gather from this assessment will allow you to decide if you can use *psychotherapy* or *behavioral intervention* to solve the presenting problems.

Chapter nineteen

INTERVENTIONS

Assessment is useless unless there is consistent communication and documentation to all members of the care giving staff regarding the evaluations and findings. Document and disseminate this valuable information. Once the behavioral assessment is completed and communicated, it's time to formulate an intervention plan.

Although the intervention techniques in this book are proven and effective, remember that everyone is different, and what works for one person may not work for another. Also, what works during one time of day may be ineffective at another time. In addition, because some people deteriorate over time, what once worked may eventually become ineffective.

THE INTERVENTION PLAN

Begin with one of the problem behaviors, and formulate goals for modifying the behavior.

1. List the probable and possible causes of the problem behaviors.

Behavioral Objectives

At the end of this section readers will be able to

List the component of an intervention plan

Define the elements of intervention

Discuss the steps in a thorough behavioral intervention plan

Communicate effectively with people exhibiting problem behaviors

2. Assess what goals are within the person's ability to attain.

3. Describe the specific interventions that will be used.

4. Define treatment goals and time limits for the intervention plan.

5. All staff needs to be involved in the treatment plan.

Notify everyone involved in treatment of the plan. Do this in writing, and follow up by telling them verbally. All staff on all shifts must be aware of the treatment plan.

6. Implement the plan for the stated time period, and assess the results.

- If the current treatment goals have been met, set new goals that approach the criteria for the termination of treatment.

- If the treatment goals have not been met, assess the reasons.

Has the treatment team carried out the plan in a consistent and conscientious manner? Are the goals within the resident's current capacity? If not, new goals must be set. In this case return to step two.

7. When treatment goals are achieved, the intervention is complete.

ELEMENTS OF INTERVENTION

All behavioral interventions should contain the following elements:

- *Acknowledgment*: Tell the person that you recognize they are having a problem. One of the most common complaints of elderly people is that their problems are discounted or ignored.

- *Validation*: Validation it the act of letting the person know they have a right to feel as they do. Is should be done whether or not their feeling are reality based. If the person is delusional, agree with their delusional statement, and redirect them.

- *Problem solving*: Help the person come up with some solutions to their stated problem. Document all attempts at problem solving, so that the person has a record of what has been done, and so others do not waste time trying what has not worked.

- *Reinforcement*: Reward any behavior that approaches or resembles your goal.

- *Consequences*: Let the person know about the logical consequences of unwanted behavior. Remove any rewards for the behavior you wish to eliminate.

KNOW THE PERSON

To do effective interventions, you must get to know the person with whom you are working. Before you begin working with anyone get the person's medical history. If the patient is in a hospital or skilled nursing facility, go through the chart thoroughly. Ask the staff members what they know about the person. If possible, talk to the family members, and get as much background information as you can.

Ask about the person's education, job, hobbies, religion, political affiliation, likes and dislikes. Ask about their personality, their temperament, their pet peeves, their skills and their shortcomings. Become as

Steps to behavioral intervention

1. Get a thorough history

2. Assess & rule out medical problems

3. Assess & rule out medication problems

4. Assess cognitive functioning

5. Identify problem behaviors

   log:
   frequency
   severity
   antecedents
   consequences

6. Formulate intervention plan

7. Implement plan

   change antecedents
   change consequences
   educate
   psychotherapy

8. Assess effectiveness of intervention

   If not successful:
   re-assess goals
   re-assess capacity to respond to goals

   If successful, terminate intervention

1904 Teddy Roosevelt elected
1905
1906
1907
1908 Ford builds Model T
1909
1910
1911
1912
1913
1914 World War I begins
1916 Woodrow Wilson elected
1917
1918 World War I ends
1919 Prohibition begins
1920
1921
1922
1923
1924
1925
1926
1927
1928 Herbert Hoover elected
1929
1930
1931
1932
1933
1934
1935
1936
1937 Chinese Resist Japanese
1938
1939
1940
1941 Pearl Harbor attacked
1942
1943
1944
1945 Japan Surrenders
1946 Philippine Independence
1949 China Occupied
1950 Korean war begins
1951
1952
1953 Korean war ends
1954
1955 advent of TV
1956

familiar with them as possible before you attempt to implement any behavioral intervention. Match your interventions with the person's level of functioning.

ACKNOWLEDGE AGE DIFFERENCES

Because all of us have a tendency to group elderly people into the general category of "old," we fail to make generational distinctions between older adults. We have no trouble seeing that a twenty year old is from a different generation than a forty year old, but a sixty year old is seldom differentiated from and eighty year old.

There are however, substantial differences. An eighty year old is, in fact, from a different generation than a sixty year old, and these differences must be acknowledged.

To get a clear perspective of who you are dealing with, it is often helpful to look at the year a person was born. A person born in 1900 will have had a much different life experience than someone born in 1930.

Consider what year it was when the person graduated from high school, and entered the world of work. Things were immensely different for a worker in 1920 than they were in 1950. Post-war America was economically and socially a different place than prewar culture, and the values, beliefs and preferences of each generation were vastly different. Be aware of these factors when talking to someone.

APPROACH

How you approach a person is the most important factor in how they will respond to you. For example, people with dementia often have severe cognitive deficits, but they are still quite able to recognize and react to emotions. They will respond to your emotional tone even if they cannot understand what you are saying. When you display impatience and irritation, those feelings will be imparted to the resident, and he or she will respond in kind.

When approaching a person, show a positive, friendly attitude. Always approach slowly, and from the front. Don't take negative responses personally. Do not over-react to unusual behavior. Be responsive, not reactive.

Ask the person how they wish to be addressed. Some people prefer to be formerly addressed. Researcher Barbara Wilson illustrates why this can be important.

> C.W was a patient that became densely amnesic in 1985. The staff members are always seen by him as strangers, no matter how long they have cared for him. A formal greeting was less unnerving for him than demonstrable affection from perceived strangers.

VERBAL INSTRUCTION

People with hearing problems or dementia often have difficulty understanding and comprehending what is said to them. Dementia may prevent them from understanding words, or recognizing common objects and people. They may also have a difficult time separating reality from delusion.

1. Always use a calm, soothing voice and gentle touch.

2. Identify yourself by name, role and function.

For example: "Hello, Mrs. Stevens. My name is Dr. Cone. I'm a psychologist, and I'm here to help you with any problems you are having."

3. Speak slowly and clearly, and give the person ample time to respond.

Older people may need a longer period of time to comprehend and respond to what is being said.

4. Use simple language, concrete terms, and concepts that the person can understand.

5. Use positives, not negatives.

Tell the person what you want them to do, not what you don't want them to do. Avoid negative commands like, "Don't do that." This infantalizes people and provokes anger.

6. Match your tone of voice, posture, and demeanor with what you are saying.

People understand messages more clearly if your actions correspond with what you are saying.

7. Do not offer choices or ask questions when it's not necessary.

For example, say, "Its time to go to dinner," not, "Would you like to eat now?"

8. Help a person complete a thought or sentence when it is apparent that they are stuck.

9. Respond to the person's emotions, and do not attempt to correct misperceptions.

It is seldom helpful to point out to a person that they are deluded—if they have memory problems they will soon forget anything they are told. If they do not, they will include you in the delusion and come to see you as an enemy.

A better tactic is to validate the person's feelings,

and not worry about the reality of what is being said. For example, if they tell you, "I'm the Captain here," say, "That must make you feel important," not, "You're not the Captain."

NON VERBAL INTERVENTIONS

When helping a person to master a new task, use the following steps. When considering the non-verbal component of a message, do the following:

1. Stand directly in the person's line of sight. Assume an equal or lower stance than their's.

2. Make eye contact.

3. Move slowly. Quick movements sometimes scare people.

4. Break down all tasks into simple steps.

5. Implement the beginning of each task by showing the person how to begin.

Give behavioral cues. For example, put a hair brush in the resident's hand and begin the brushing. The person's motor program will take over after this

If the tasks are too difficult, the person may become agitated and resistant. If so, re-assess the person's abilities.

6. Provide opportunities for the person to succeed at tasks.

The primary goal of all activity is to build confidence and self esteem. Reward and reinforce any success.

7. Do not do things for a person simply to save time.

Because you have many things to do, and may be

rushed for time, this is often tempting, However, this infantalizes the person, and will lead to more demands for care giving .

8. Do not rush a or pressure a person to complete a task.

Instead, observe how long it takes them to do something, record this information, and allow ample time in the resident's schedule.

9. Give the person as much control of their life as possible.

Assist, guide and educate, but do not dominate.

10. Limit distractions in the environment.

When teaching a skill, turn off televisions and radios. Close the door. Give instructions to other staff not to interrupt.

11. Use distractions to refocus and redirect the person during any care giving task that may increase unwanted behavior.

12. Do not force a person to anything against her will.

Leave the area and return to try again later. When you return explain once more what you are going to do.

13. Anticipate the person's needs based on your knowledge of her or him.

Take the time to learn their schedule, their needs, and their personal preferences, and you will greatly increase cooperation.

Chapter twenty

MANAGING SPECIFIC BEHAVIOR PROBLEMS

CATASTROPHIC REACTION

A *catastrophic reaction* is an uncontrolled emotional outburst—a response to a feelings of overwhelming helplessness. Catastrophic reactions include crying, yelling, outbursts of anger, flailing arms and legs, and hitting.

Brain injured people (particularly in the left, dominant hemisphere) often respond to questions or tasks which are cognitively demanding with catastrophic reactions. Sixteen percent of people with dementia exhibit this behavior, and it's also frequent in acute stroke—in particular after subarachnoid hemorrhages and cerebral infarcts. It is strongly related with post-stroke depression.

In most cases the person will be unaware of why they are becoming agitated, possibly because of disconnection syndromes and implicit memory problems. These reactions are most common in patients with aphasia.

Behavioral Objectives

At the end of this section readers will be able to

List common behavior problems

Diccuss the causes of these problems

Assess the antecedents of these problems

Intervene to correct or decrease the incidence of the problems

**Causes of
Catastrophic Reactions**

Organic variables

Brain damage

(especially in the amygdala,
temporal lobes, hypothalamus and
frontal lobes)

Neurotransmitter dysfunction
(decreased serotonin levels
in the brain)

Psychologic variables

Encountering a new
environment

Realization that one is
forgetful or ill

Reduced ability to
communicate

Acting out psychotic distress

Accentuation of premorbid
personality traits

Problematic relationship to
caregiver in the past

Environmental variables

Unidentified noise

Inadequate lighting

Moving to unfamiliar places

Adversarial patient management style

These reactions occur most often in the morning, when care activity is the highest. It's during this time of day that the staff is most pressured to stay on schedule and complete their activities.

Because getting ready for the day is a set of complex behaviors, it can be taxing for both the staff and the person being helped. The physical contact and intrusiveness of this behavior, such as grooming and getting dressed, may be unwanted and unpleasant. Therefore the best way to avoid these reactions is to work withing the persons capacity to cope with stimulation.

When catastrophic reactions do occur:

1. Do not *react* to them, but *respond* to them.

If you see a person becoming upset by your activity, stop what you are doing.

Even though the person may attempt to hit you , the behavior is not directed at you—the person is merely frightened and trying to protect himself. Responding to this type of outburst means that you ask yourself, "What's my goal here?" rather than thinking, "Omigod, what do I do now?" or yelling at the person, "What's the matter with you? I'm only trying to do my job!" The goal is to help the person calm down.

2. Allow the staff member with the best relationship with the resident respond to the reaction.

Rapport with a recognized caregiver can do a lot to calm someone down.

3. Approach the person calmly, and speak softly.

4. Do not attempt to talk the person out of

the reaction.

5. If appropriate, use touch to establish contact.

6. Give reassurance.

7. Refocus the person with an object or another topic.

8. If necessary, guide the person to a quiet place for a time out.

9. Do not call attention to the behavior.

10. If all else fails, leave the room and back later.

RESISTING CARE

Patients who resist care cause problems and frustrate staff and other residents. When a person consistently resists care, schedules are disrupted, and sometimes tempers flare. Staff members get frustrated when their efforts to be helpful are rebuffed.

Studies show that people are most likely to resist care when they are approached by more than two people at a time. Resistance to care also occurs when caregiving activities are done too rapidly or roughly, or when the care giving is done to fit the staff's needs, not the resident's.

Some people resist care because they fear being hurt. Often, they resent the fact that they can no longer care for themselves, and project their feelings of anger at the staff. Like a young child—who's greatest power is to be disruptive—many elderly people see the refusal to accept care as the only power they retain.

Types of Resisting Care

Noncompliant Eating

eating foreign objects or materials
refusing to eat
choking due to bolting food down
eating foods not permitted on diet
eating excessively

Noncompliant Drinking

the use of alcohol
refusing to drink liquids
drinking toxic liquid (shaving lotion, etc.)
excessive intake of liquids
drinking liquids not permitted on diet
not drinking liquids on one's own

Noncompliant Smoking

smoking excessively
careless use of cigarettes
careless use of matches
smoking against medical advice
smoking in unauthorized places

Abuse of Medication

refusing medications
hiding when medications are given out
hoarding medications
overdosing
taking unauthorized medications
using illicit drugs

Those with dementia may resist care because they no longer realize the meaning of daily activities like bathing or taking medication.

Resisting care, refusing to eat, and refusing to take needed medication can also be signs of *silent suicide,* an unstated attempt to end one's life. This resistance has also been called *indirect self-destructive behavior* (ISDB).

BEHAVIORAL INTERVENTIONS FOR RESISTING CARE

1. Have one staff member establish rapport and be the primary care giver.

2. Avoid situations that are antecedents to resistant behavior.

3. Distract the person when engaging in a behavior that has caused resistance.

4. Allow the person as much autonomy as possible.

5. Put something in the person's hands to occupy them.

6. Assess them for depression and suicidal ideation.

BATHING PROBLEMS

When I was a child, I was taught to take a bath each night before bed. After the bath, I was often rewarded with hot chocolate and a story. This was always a special time of day for me, and for many of us, bathing is still one of life's special pleasures.

But this is not true for many elderly people who need help with bathing. Bathing raises issues of privacy, independence, and personal space.

Bathing an elderly person is frequently a time consuming and difficult task. In fact, researchers Sloane and Mathew found that bathing elderly people required more time and more supervision than any other activity of daily living, and professional care givers say that the amount of time spent on bathing patients equals or surpasses the amount of time spent on any other job assignment.

Some residents interpret bath time as being stripped naked in order to be harmed. When this happens they become agitated and fearful. Keep in mind that elderly people need not bathe every day, as frequent bathing can dry and crack aged skin.

1. Ask family members about the person's bathing habits, preferences, and usual time of bathing.

Find out if they prefer baths or showers. If at all possible, develop a bathing schedule that resembles the person's preferences.

2. Give baths only when necessary.

Be sure bathing is within the care guidelines of your state, but don't over bathe a person.

The most common fears about bathing

Being naked in front of strangers

Being lifted into the tub

Getting in and out of tub

Noises that the tub makes

Water in the tub

The tub itself

Mechanical devices on the tub

Common behavioral problems during bathing

resisting care

yelling or screaming

restlessness

verbal aggression

talking to self

physical aggression

catastrophic reaction

throwing things

3. Be cognizant of the person's self consciousness about nudity and need for dignity.

Allow them as much privacy as possible. Use same sex caregivers whenever possible. Research on bathing shows that patients become most resistant when stripped of their clothing, seated on a cold, metal, mechanical chair, and restrained with a safety belt

4. Do not ask the person to undress until they are in the bathroom.

6. Make the room temperature and the water temperature comfortable.

7. If the person is demented, introduce them to the idea of bathing gradually.

Many problems associated with bathing are caused by a lack of understanding by staff of the behavior of people with cognitive impairment and dementia. Instead of perceiving bathing as a single activity, the task goes better if it's seen as a series of independent steps that require specific instructions and attention to each exhibited behavior as it occurs. For example:

Take the person into the bathroom and let them hear and see the running water.

Allow them to get undressed.

Help them get in the tub or shower.

Give them a washcloth and let them begin to wash themselves. This engages motor programs that do not involve working memory.

8. Do not get in arguments about bathing.

Proceed slowly, step-by-step. If the person resists, don't argue—try again later. Negative experiences during bathing have an undesirable effect on the relationship between the patient and staff, which can last throughout the day. Repeated negative bathing experiences can result in permanently alienating the staff from the patient.

9. Take personal items such as favorite soaps, bath oils, towels, and wash cloths into the bathroom to make the surroundings more familiar and inviting.

People experience discomfort entering a room that does not resemble a bathroom or any other homelike bathing area.

10. Shampoo the person's hair last.

This allows less of a chance for soap in the eyes or discomfort from dripping hair.

11. When all else fails, use sponge-baths.

Remember that the goal is to get the person clean, not to get them to obey you.

EATING PROBLEMS

Lost in uncongenial surroundings, fed on unfamiliar food, they sickened, became inefficient, and were then allowed to crawl away and rest.

Joseph Conrad, *Heart of Darkness.*

People have eating problems for a variety of reasons. For example, almost half of people between ages 75 and 80 years have lost much or all of their sense of smell, and therefore have decreased flavor and odor perception. This decline in the sense of smell and taste is a normal result of aging, but it can also be made worse by disease and other factors, such as medication side-effects.

Dietary analysis of people with taste and smell problems show that their food intake differs significantly from those who don't have these problems. For example, most of them had a lowered preference for strongly sour or bitter foods and ate fewer citrus fruits and vegetables.

Researchers have also found that women with reduced functioning of the senses of taste and smell eat more saturated fat. Men have a less acute sense of taste and smell than women throughout their life, and may respond differently to the age-related decline than women.

Other people don't eat well because they have difficulty chewing and swallowing due to dental problems or neurological damage. Still others may have no appetite because they are depressed.

There is also evidence that dementia may actually damage the parts of the brain that regulate hunger, rendering the person unable to feel the need to eat. In addition, people with advanced dementia may no longer be able to comprehend the complex task of eating. Even

Factors affecting taste and smell

Alzheimer's disease

Parkinson's disease

Renal failure

Upper respiratory infection

Smoking

Bronchial asthma

Diabetes mellitus

Certain medications (antidepressants, valium)

Zinc and niacin deficiency

Vitamin B_{12} deficiency

though all of these factors cause eating problems, the most common reason for people refusing to eat is simply because they do not like the food. This can be because they have certain food preferences that are not being met, or because the food is bad.

Complaining about food is one of the most common complaints that I hear from long-term care residents. Put yourself in the resident's place. Imagine no longer being able to enjoy any of your favorite foods. Every day of your life, three times a day, you are served something you didn't ask for and don't like. It's not surprising that food is the source of many problems in a long term care facility.

Eating is an important part of life, and consistently poor food can lead to a great deal of unhappiness and disruptive behavior. This is a relatively easy problem to correct, and is usually well worth the effort. Even something as simple as giving residents two options for a meal can increase satisfaction.

BEHAVIORAL INTERVENTIONS FOR EATING PROBLEMS

1. Experiment with various food textures.

Because of deficits in smell and taste, texture may be the only enjoyment of eating.

2.Enhance the flavor of the food

Adding flavor to food can improve food intake. A group of elderly men and women living in a retirement home ate more food and improved their immune function when several foods at each meal were enhanced with either meat, cheese or maple flavoring.

Bacon flavor also increases food consumption,

especially when added to vegetables. Fruit flavors and sauces increase the consumption of chicken and pork. The ability to detect carrot aroma falls dramatically in the aged, and concentrated carrot essence increases the amount of carrots eaten.

Butter flavoring and extracts such as almond and lemon help also. Twice the amount of extract called for in a recipe should enhance flavor. Herbs and spices should also be doubled. Lifting the cover from the food just before the person begins to eat releases concentrated food aromas and increases appetite.

3. Be aware of the resident's cultural and ethnic food preferences, and honor them when possible.

4. Learn about the resident's prior eating habits and food preferences.

Ask the person or family members about idiosyncratic eating habits.

5. Minimize all noises and other stimuli that distract the resident from focusing on eating.

6. To minimize confusion, limit the number of foods served at one time, and the number of utensils.

7. Stroke the residents arm gently while they are eating,

Several studies show that this simple intervention increases food intake in people with dementia.

8. Assess for paranoia.

Paranoid people often refuse to eat because they think their food is being poisoned. Giving them canned food sometimes helps, as they think it is less likely to have been tampered with.

9. Sometimes it is necessary to feed the person

SLEEP PROBLEMS

As people age the quality and quantity of sleep decreases. Sleep problems in the elderly include problems falling asleep, problems staying asleep, and early morning awakening.

Residents who wake up during the night are at high risk for injury. Sleep problems are disruptive to staff and to other residents. The most common reasons for sleep problems in the elderly are too much napping, pain, and the need to go to the bathroom.

BEHAVIORAL INTERVENTIONS FOR SLEEP PROBLEMS

1. Become aware of the resident's sleep habits and sleep difficulties.

2. Ask the resident and family members about the residents sleep habits.

3. Establish a regimented bedtime, and bedtime routine.

4. When a person awakens during the night, re-orient them to time and place, and calm them.

A gentle touch and soothing voice are effective methods of calming.

5. When a person repeatedly gets out of bed and disturbs others, guide her to a place where disturbance is minimized.

6. When a resident is not able to return to sleep, place her near the nurse's station and give her something to do.

7. Provide plenty of activity during the day.

This improves sleep quality and reduces napping.

8. Eliminate caffeine and other stimulants.

Elderly people metabolize caffeine very slowly. One cup of coffee a day can cause sleep problems. In the elderly, it may take up to six hours to eliminate the caffeine in a cup of coffee. Also, check to see that none of the medications they are taking contain caffeine. Antidepressants potentiate caffeine, and the antibiotic *Cipro* can increase caffeine levels drastically.

9. Have them go to the bathroom just before bedtime.

10. Furnish bedtime snacks to alleviate blood sugar problems.

11. Do not set bedtime too early.

12. A good proportion of sleep problems are caused by minor aches and pains.

A simple analgesic like aspirin can improve sleep quality.

13. Make sure the person gets at least one half our of morning sun every day.

This increases melatonin. It there is no sunlight, use light panels.

DANGEROUS MOVES

Falls and injuries can be deadly to frail and elderly people. In fact, half of the hospital beds for trauma patients are occupied by people suffering hip fractures caused by falls. At least twenty percent of the elderly women suffering hip fractures in this country die within one year if the accident as a result of complications of the injury, making fractures from osteoporosis the 12th lead-ing cause of death in the United States.

Injuries in the elderly also occur because of general weakness, degenerative muscle disease, balance dis-orders, impaired motor function, medication problems, impaired judgement, memory loss, sensory loss, and problems with depth-perception.

Victims of strokes in the right hemisphere are often paralyzed on the left side of the body—unable to move the left arm, leg and foot, and unable to walk.

However, they exhibit a *complete denial* of any disa-bility. The denial of paralysis is caused by the loss of a particular brain system that allows them to have aware-ness of their internal body map. In severe cases, the ina-bility to sense this defect through the body's sensory system is permanent.

The difficulty with these patients is that, lacking any awareness that they are paralyzed on one side, they often attempt to stand, walk, or engage in other activity that can result in falls or injuries. In some cases people may hurt themselves by actually attempting to throw the unwanted, paralyzed limb out of bed. Others may attempt to injure the limb on order to get rid of it. These patients need to be frequently confronted with their disability, so that they come to know that there is something wrong,

Fall prevention checklist

Gather data from all sources—the resident, family, all nursing shifts, and other staff.

Occurence

Is there a pattern to the resident's falls?
same time of day
same place
same situation (e.g. fails out of bed)

Check for

Medication problems
Orthostatic hypotension
Delirium
Confusion
Infection
Weakness.
Blood sugar abnormality
Urine test abnormality
Occult blood
Blood pressure changes

Activity

Was the person
- doing anything new or unusual
- standing
- walking
- getting in or out of wheelchair
- getting in or out of bed
- responding to a bowel or bladder need
- reaching for food or water
- reaching for a call light

Fall prevention checklist

Environment

Was the person
   in a crowd
   In a noisy place
   on a wet floor
   in an unfamiliar place
   stumbling on an object in
      his path
   restrained

Personal impairments

Was the person

   having vision or hearing
      difficulty
   uncomfortable in any way
   (e.g. in a wheelchair, bed,
      chair, walker, etc.)
   wearing shoes properly fit
      and tied
   wearing clothing properly
   agitated, frightened, or
      angry
   in any pain
   suffering from motor or gait
      difficulties
   suffering from neurological
      damage
   cognitively impaired
   dizzy, weak or faint

but even frequent reminders don't work in some cases.

Transitions from wheelchairs to beds are often sources of unsafe movements an injury. Many people with physical limitations insist on getting out of bed unassisted, and therefore fall. Poles by the side of the bed can be helpful in these cases. If the person cannot get in or out of the bed safely, he can slide down the pole without injury. The use of alarms can warn caregivers when a person is attempting to get up.

Physical restraint has often been considered as the only recourse to prevent unsafe movement, but because it is restrictive, it can lead to other problems such as agitation. In addition, it has also been shown that in many cases, restraint actually *increases* the number of injuries, because care givers use restraints as a substitute for careful observation and protection. Because of these factors, restraint should be used as a last resort, and not as a replacement for monitoring unsafe movement.

BEHAVIORAL INTERVENTIONS FOR UNSAFE MOVEMENTS

1. Assess the person's potential for self-harm and falling.

2. Observe the person to see what unsafe movements they exhibit.

3. See if the person can walk and talk at the same time.

People who have to stop walking to talk, a condition known as *walk and talk syndrome*, are at increased risk of falling.

4. When a person is about to do something unsafe, do not yell at them or run towards them.

This can frighten them and cause injury. Instead, approach them calmly and remove tem from harm.

5. Refocus them while you remove them from danger.

For example, offer the person an object so that they loosen their grip on a chair or bed rail.

6. Never rush or pressure a person to do something.

7. Make sure that shoes are on properly, and shoelaces are tied.

8. Use non-skid shoes.

9. Make sure all clothing is put on properly.

Eliminate ties, scarves, and belts.

10. Clean up spills immediately.

11. Do not move objects in the residents room.

12. Use night lights.

13. Use position-change alarms and wander-guards when necessary.

14. Teach safe transfer methods to all staff.

Unsafe and uncomfortable transfers are a not only one of the most common complaint of people receiving care, they are also one of the major causes of injuries.

15. Place banners or ribbons across door-ways to off and unsafe limit areas.

16. Install handrails in all hallways.

People with dementia may sometimes harm themselves by biting, scratching or rubbing. As this is often done as a means of self stimulation, it is useful to refocus them on another less harmful behavior. Here is an example:

An 82-year-old female resident of a nursing home diagnosed with advanced Alzheimer's disease had been biting her finger incessantly for the past year. On examination, her digit was bitten to the bone.

Attempts at wrapping her finger and placing mittens on one hand and then both hands were unsuccessful.

Various pharmacologic agents, including clonazepam, thiothixene, thioridazine, trazodone, propranolol, carbamazepine, and buspirone, were administered with no success. Having observed that some patients with Alzheimer's disease appear to make chewing movements without food in the mouth, we used chewing gum in an attempt to distract the patient from chewing on her finger. Within 24 hours of instituting the gum, the finger biting ceased. Over the next 6 months there were no recurrences of finger biting, and no episodes of swallowing the gum or aspiration were noted.

COMPLAINING AND ATTENTION SEEKING

Every one has complaints at times. But unwarranted complaining—complaining that has little basis in reality—is bothersome, irritating and disruptive. And when a patient and staff members develop a negative relationship, everyone suffers. When staff members become irritated with a person, it affects caregiving. In addition, like the boy who cried wolf, the incessantly complaining person soon becomes shunned and ignored, creating the potential for legitimate complaints to be missed.

Complaining usually consists of constant concerns about health, quality of care, and dissatisfactions with other residents. But most complaining is a result of depression, low self-esteem, under-stimulation, and inadvertent reinforcement of negative behavior.

Attention seeking consist of the person constantly requesting that they talk to a staff member about something vitally important

BEHAVIORAL INTERVENTIONS FOR COMPLAINING AND ATTENTION SEEKING

1. Listen to and assess the validity of the person's request or complaint.

If the complaint seems valid, find a remedy.

2. Make sure that complaints about pain and discomfort are checked out thoroughly.

3. Set limits on complaining, and attention seeking, inform the resident of the limits.

4. Don't ask a complaint prone resident how he feels.

5. Reinforce positive behavior.

6. Increase the resident's social stimulation.

7. Make a list of the positive things that the person is willing to talk about.

Give the list to all staff to use. When the person begin's to complain, start talking about one of these topics.

8. Do not reward complaining with special attention.

9. Give the resident a complaint form to fill out.

Keep a file of the person's complaints and the actions taken to remedy them. When a complaint reoccurs, show it to the person, and remind them of what has been dome to help remedy the problem.

10. Set aside a specific time to listen to the person, and inform them that you will be available at that time.

MANIPULATION AND SPLITTING

People with emotional and personality disorders are often manipulative, dishonest, and devaluing. On the other hand, people with dementia, though difficult at times, are not often deliberately manipulative. For this reason when assessing for manipulation, it's important to know the resident's cognitive status.

If the resident shows manipulative behavior and has only minimal signs of dementia, screen them for personality disorder. The most common personality disorders that include manipulative behavior are the *narcissistic*, *borderline*, and *antisocial* personality disorders.

There are many types of manipulative behavior, but the most common and most disruptive is *splitting*. Splitting is often used to disrupt treatment. It involves a resident assessing the defenses and weaknesses of each staff member, and systematically playing the staff against one another. Soon the staff find themselves fighting with each other about things they have been told by the resident. This behavior undermines the sense of teamwork, and diverts attention away from the resident.

> In one of the facilities where I was consulting, an elderly gentleman named George actually got three staff members fired. Over time, George would gain the confidence of one staff member, and then tell them that other staff members were complaining about them. He would then do the same thing with other staff. Soon he had the staff talking behind one another's back, gossiping, and sabotaging each other's work. Before long, fights would break out, and someone would eventually get fired.

This behavior continued for almost a year before I

was called in to develop an intervention plan. Although each situation must be handled differently, here are some general guidelines tp prevent manipulation and splitting.

BEHAVIORAL INTERVENTIONS FOR MANIPULATION

1. Give the person as much independence as possible.

People often become manipulative when they feel they have no other power.

2. Be very clear about non-compliant behavior, manipulative behavior, and its consequences.

Tell the resident what the results of their actions will be. For example, "Mrs. Gibby, you do not have to come to lunch, but there will be no food available later when you get hungry."

3. When a person begins to complain about another staff member, get the staff member, and have the three of you work out the problem.

This is very effective in reducing splitting.

YELLING AND SCREAMING

Yelling and screaming disturbs other residents as well as staff. These behaviors may occur because of over-stimulation, or a response to demands beyond the per-son's capacity. However, these behaviors also occur as a result of under-stimulation and boredom. Some residents may yell and scream for self-stimulation, or to get atten-tion, while others do so because of genuine pain, dis-comfort, hunger, anxiety or depression.

BEHAVIORAL INTERVENTIONS FOR YELLING AND SCREAMING

1. Assess the cause.

Determine the time, place, and frequency of the be-haviors, and see if there is a pattern.

2. Ask the person what is wrong.

3. As an immediate intervention, give the person something to eat or to suck on.

4. Distract the person by talking about something that interests them.

5. Provide comfort by physical touch.

6. Play soothing music.

7. Provide the person with a comforting or stimulating object such as a stuffed animal.

8. If it is determined that the cause is over-stimulation, relocate the person to a quiet room.

9. If it is determined that the cause is under-stimulation, increase the person's opportunity for social contact.

10. Break the reinforcement cycle.

Give the person attention when they are not yelling or screaming, and ignore the behavior when it occurs.

11. When all else fails, move the person to a place where the disruption to others is minimized.

VERBAL AGGRESSION

Verbally aggressive behavior includes arguing, threatening, swearing, and demeaning others. This behav-ior may be a result of resisting care, fighting, or be a component of a catastrophic reaction. Anything that exceeds the resident's coping ability can trigger verbal aggression.

In some cases, verbal aggression may be a person's only form of expressing anger and frustration about his or her condition. Verbally aggressive or abusive behavior may also be used as a defense against loneliness and emotional pain. The person may feel that being abusive will distance others, and therefore save them from having to deal with their true feelings.

> Mrs. Nickerson had a reputation in the facility for being cranky, abusive, and generally unpleasant. Many of the staff avoided working with her because of her abrasive manner. However, it was discovered that this was her way of distancing people to protect herself from her feelings of worthlessness, loneliness, and fears of abandonment. Inside she was thinking, "I'll reject you before you have a chance to reject me." Ignoring her initial abuse and confronting her feelings of loneliness ended the problem.

In people with dementia or other forms of cognitive impairment, impulse control is impaired. Because they no longer have the means to prevent themselves from acting on impulse, anger is immediately and bluntly expressed.

BEHAVIORAL INTERVENTIONS FOR VERBAL AGGRESSION

1. Don't attempt to settle an argument or

reason with an angry person.

Angry people are irrational, and are poor problem solvers. Talking to them when they are raging will only escalate them, and worsen the problem. Instead, talk about the behavior when it is not happening, and offer a more constructive solution.

2. Distract the person.

Ignore the abusive behavior and ask a question about an unrelated subject.

3. Approach the person calmly.

Touch is usually calming, but know the resident's capacity for assaultive behavior. Don't put yourself in harm's way.

4. If the verbal aggression is directed towards you, do not take it personally, and do not react to it.

Ignore the behavior, and reflect an attitude of caring. If this does not work, and the abusive person is in no danger, leave the room.

5. If a person is consistently being verbally abusive towards you, become aware of the ways you may be inadvertently reinforcing the behavior.

Some residents get satisfaction out of getting staff upset. If you are visibly upset by the abusive behavior, you are encouraging the resident to repeat it.

AGITATION

Agitation is the most frequent reason for a behavioral consultation. Agitation may be caused by many things, but it's usually a by-product of cognitive impairment related to brain damage or dementia.

Agitation may also be caused by over-stimulation, or the person's inability to comprehend what is required of her.

Getting agitated can also be a result of frustration about the loss of freedom and choice that elders experience when living in a group environment.

Put yourself in their shoes for a moment Think of checking in to a hotel. As soon as you arrive, you are assigned a room. When you open the door, you see two other people whom you've never seen before. You are told they are your roommates, and you should get ready for bed.

The next morning, you are told to get out of bed because you will miss your breakfast. When you reach the dining room, you are given a meal that you didn't order, and don't want. You ask to send it back but are told that's your only choice. Getting irritated yet?.

Keep this in mind when working with agitated patients. If you feel the person is in a receptive state, validate their feelings and protect their self-esteem. For example you might say, "I can see that you are frustrated, and I understand why. This would be aggravating to anyone."

Although agitation is a common problem in dementia, it must be remembered that most negative behavior occurs because it is inadvertently reinforced by

The most common forms of agitation

• restlessness

• pacing

• complaining

• perseveration

• repeating the same words

• chronic negativity

• chronic attention seeking

• swearing

• verbally abusive language

others. Negative behavior attracts attention. Elderly patients who feel alone & neglected will do anything to get attention, and agitation is a very effective way to accomplish this.

When you see someone becoming agitated, your best bet is to leave a once or provide them access to a quiet place. People with memory impairments soon forget what disturbed them.

Use verbal and nonverbal communication that enhances feelings of safety and lowers fear. When supportive, empathic verbal skills are combined with active listening, most patients, even those who are demented or psychotic, respond..This can be quite effective in defusing anxiety and hostility.

The person should be encouraged to express his feelings, and redirect their activities in order to distract the patient from anxiety.

Keep communications short and simple. Interactions should be directed at validating the person;'s feelings, and increasing their self- esteem, while decreasing anxiety.

When agitation is reduced, channeling anxiety in positive ways will facilitate continued de-escalation. Every stage and step are critical because patient behaviors can escalate rapidly to assault, or de-escalate if effectively managed. If the patient begins to de-escalate, nurses need to constantly monitor patient's behavior until it is stable.

Aggression is also a way to overcome feelings of vulnerability powerlessness. The aggressive response is primitive and instinctive. It has the same origin as a cat arching its back and making its hair stand on end. The message is, "Leave me alone."

Just like the angry cat, agitated people need more personal space because of their heightened perception and increased vigilance. Respecting personal space promotes feelings of safety and security.

Be aware that the more agitated a person becomes, the less ability they have to concentrate, think clearly, or consider the consequences of their actions. Threatened people think survival, not consequences.

BEHAVIORAL INTERVENTIONS FOR AGITATION

1. Ask the person what is agitating them.

Although they may not always know, this is often the most direct route to intervention. If the person is able to tell you what is bothering them, take steps to remove the source of the problem, or help the person cope with the difficulty. If they cannot tell you,

2. Do a complete assessment to establish the person's cognitive skills, memory function, and emotional state.

This will allow you to assess what kind of intervention would be most effective.

3. Check to see if there have been any recent medication changes, or a change in the person's health.

4. Observe and record what happened immediately before the problem behavior.

This will allow you to assess what triggers the behavior, and possibly eliminate the triggers.

5. Withdraw all reinforcers for the problem

behaviors.

This often means removing the person from the area in which the agitation occurred. It is sometimes necessary to move them to a quiet room for time out. This also may require ignoring the agitation, as it is sometimes used to get attention.

6. Provide the person with structured daily activities

People with cognitive impairment do not tolerate change well. Because thinking and memory are impaired, new surroundings and new events are confusing and upsetting.

7. Implement negative consequences for problem behaviors.

Explain to the person that the behavior is unacceptable, and that certain privileges may be withdrawn if it persists. Negative consequences work in people with mild to moderate dementia, but are ineffective in those with serious cognitive impairment.

Chapter Twenty-one
Assault

Mrs. Donner had just arrived at the inpatient unit when I was called in to do an evaluation. When I looked in her admission notes, they read "Reason for admission: assault." I asked her, as I always do, "Why are you here?" to which she quickly replied, "Well, the damn nurse or whatever she is was trying to make me eat, and I wasn't hungry. She tried to grab my hand, so I hit her."

Assault is the targeted use of physical force that may harm other people. Assaults include hitting, grabbing, pushing, slapping, stabbing, or throwing things at another person. However, threats of assault and verbal abuse should also be considered part of assaultive behavior, as they significantly change the climate of caregiving. Unfortunately, as Mrs Donner pointed out, many assaults occur in the process of helping others.

THE INCIDENCE OF ASSAULT

Assault is an all too common problem in care facilities. While over a third of geriatric patients in nursing homes will engage in verbal assaults, physically assaultive behaviors occur in about 10 percent. But in geropsychiatric hospitals, where patients are more

Factors that contribute to Assault

Physiological Factors

physical illness
infections
electrolyte imbalances
epilepsy
temporal lobe abnormalities
medical toxicity
reactions to drugs
paradoxical drug reactions
substance abuse
drug withdrawal
dementia
fronto-temporal dementia
hallucinations
dehydration
constipation
sleep-deprivation

Psychological factors

history of assault
restlessness
agitation
disorientation
low frustration tolerance
impulse control problems
personality disorder
mental instability
schizophrenia
delusions
restrictions on behavior
recent significant loss

acutely disturbed, over 20 percent of the patients commit assault.

Unfortunately, even though assaults can be harmful to patients and to caregivers, most assaults are never reported. In fact, during a one-year study in a nursing home, researchers found that out of 1,108 incidents only 203 were actually reported.

Surveys of nursing staff have shown that many of these events go unreported because the staff has become habituated to assaults, that is, the assaults happen so frequently that they begin to accept this behavior as unavoidable and routine.

Some staff members feel that if they report assaults, they will be seen as the perpetrators, not the victims. Many nurses have stated that they don't feel that the administrators at their facilities would support them if they reported being attacked.

Even so, the most common reason that assaults are not reported is the desire to avoid the hassle of extra paper work. Overworked and over-stressed staff and administration see assault reports as one more thing to add to the pile.

The problem with this is that *not reporting assault prevents adequate prevention an intervention*, and can lead to more serious problems later—problems that affect everyone in the facility. Preventing assaults now is a prudent move to avoid injuries, complaints, and litigation later.

Rather than implement intervention programs for assault, some facilities consider assaultive residents as nuisances, and refer them elsewhere. Mrs Donner was a prime example. The facility had referred her to the hospital because they felt they could not deal with her behavior, and wanted her relocated.

THE CONSEQUENCES OF ASSAULT

Violence in your facility has profound effects on the caregiving staff—physically, emotionally and behaviorally. Physical injuries from assaults can result in black eyes, swollen jaws, scratches and bruises, ringing in the ears, hearing loss, headaches, back injuries, and in extreme cases loss of consciousness and broken bones. But although most physical injuries heal, the emotional and behavioral scars may linger on.

Researchers report that nursing staff who have been assaulted exhibit a variety of long-term emotional reactions. Although their immediate reactions are usually shock, disbelief, and self-blame, long-term reactions include feelings of helplessness, irritability, resignation, sadness, and depression.

Staff members often fear of returning to the scene of the assault and develop fear of the residents. This leads to avoidance behavior, including an avoidance of any reminders of the assault.

Some become preoccupied with thinking about the assault, and play the incident over and over in their minds. The trauma of assault also causes some staff to change their relationships with co-workers—they may become defensive, withdrawn and short tempered. There may also be an increased use of alcohol, cigarettes, or drugs. While some may also show increased absenteeism from work, loss of interest and involvement in their work, others become so traumatized that they consider a career change.

It's been my experience that staff deal with these

Factors that contribute to Assault

Environmental factors

environmental load
violation of personal space
crowding
agitated or provoked by others
excessive stimulation (e.g. noise, light, temperature and activity level)
transfer to another facility
the use of seclusion or restraints
medications without consent
family visits

Milieu Problems

staff angry at patient
staff angry at doctor
differing beliefs
differing agendas
poor documentation
failure to carry out orders
doctor doesn't respond to calls
problems with power-structure
staff conflicts
shift change problems

feelings in one of two ways—blaming themselves or blaming others. But a better approach is to put blame aside, take an objective look at the incident, and learn how to prevent it from happening again.

THE CAUSES OF ASSAULT

Environmental Factors

Robert Bigelow, author of a 1972 paper entitled *The Evolution of Cooperation, Aggression, and Self Control* concluded that, "the crowding of strangers, especially near such valuable resources as food..." was one of the major causes of human aggression. Anthony Storr, while researching the causes of aggression, found that violent behavior is most likely to occur in conditions of territoriality and social posturing. Residents often feel one-down and resentful that others are controlling their fate, and aggression is a face-saving behavior in these situations—a way to exert power and maintain control.

It's clear that Bigelow and Storr were right—because most assaults occur when there are many people in one place, when food is present, and when caregivers are most actively involved with their patients. Most assaults occur when staff members physically prompt the patient in helping them to eat, dress, shower, or move from one position to another.

In fact, assaults are most likely to occur during three peak activity periods—between 7 AM and10 AM, usually during morning preparation activities, between 12 noon and 2 PM, during and after lunch, and between 4 PM and 7 PM, during and after dinner.

Environmental Load

In his very interesting book *Public Places and Private Spaces* Dr. Albert Mehrabian explains that environments can best be described by the rate of information they contain. The rate at which this information must be processed is called *environmental load*. A *low-load environment* os one in which the amount of information we must process is small. An example of this would be an uncrowded private beach.

High-load environments include elements such as crowding, unfamiliarity, movement, and noise—just the type of environment found in many care facilities. High-load environments are known to cause a great deal of stress—they are the reason we long for that private beach so much.

As described above, high load environments occur where strangers and food are present. But of those three high load time periods, morning is the worst.

Morning is a difficult time for many of us, but for the old, frail, and cognitively impaired person, it can be hell. Reeling from the residue of two sleeping pills that have not yet metabolized, the person is rousted from his bed, prodded to get up, get dressed, and face the day. While still in a fog, the person is greeted with a flurry of activity. Even though the staff do their best to meet deadlines while at the same time being helpful, their efforts are uninvited and unwelcome. It is no surprise then that assault is often the crime of the cranky.

In many facilities, residents are often deprived of their personal space. They are often asked to share rooms and recreational space with people they do not know, and may not like. Strangers frequently enter their rooms. They are subjected to medical and care giving procedures that involve unwanted physical contact. Crowding is constant.

Nursing home patients are often unwillingly placed

The body buffer zone in most schizophrenic patients is four times larger than in a normal population in close proximity with a group of strangers, many of whom are loud, intrusive, inappropriate, unpleasant, or unde-sirable. Put too many people in a room for an extended period of time, and tempers will flair.

In fact, limited body space can create intolerable anxiety for people whose coping skills are impaired. Each person's "buffer zone" varies, and any activity that involves the invasion of the individual's personal space increases the risk for assault. The majority of assault s in long term care facilities occur because a resident is attempting to defend his or her personal space.

Be aware that the body buffer zone in cognitively impaired people is larger than in healthy people, and that in most schizophrenic patients the buffer zone is four times larger than in a normal population.

In addition to crowding, familiarity also affects environmental load—most people are more comfortable in a room with twenty others whom they know well than they are in a room full of strangers.

Keep in mind that for people with memory impairments, *the environment is always unfamiliar, which increases the load significantly*. Even though a person may have been a facility for an extended time period, residents with severe memory problems will continue to see the staff and other residents as strangers.

Noise

As people age, their ability to filter out unwanted noise decreases. While the average teenager can put themselves into a trance-like state, eliminating all outside input except MTV, elderly people are easily detracted, irritated, and can become overwhelmed by too much noise. In cognitively impaired people, excessive

The more emotional conflict there is in the staff of a facility, the more assault will occur.

noise or motion may overload their coping level and cause them to "snap". I have seen people run from the day-room because of too much noise and activity.

Structure

Routines become important to the elderly. Habit does not require thought, but change does, and therefore cognitively impaired people find change frightening and confusing. For this reason, disruption of daily routines often increases agitation. Assaults more than double between Sundays and Mondays, probably because of different activity schedules, different staff, and the after effects of weekend visits from friends and family.

At Atascadero State Hospital in California researchers Carmel and Hunter found that the transition between the relatively low level of activity on weekends and the higher level of activity on the weekdays may contribute to assaults.

Assaults more than double between Sundays and Mondays

But even though structure is good, too much structure is not. Many residents may become angry about schedules and treatment regimens that are contrary to their wishes.

In an effort to impose structure, some caregivers put great emphasis on the maintenance of institutional rules and routines. When patients did not cooperate with the pre-ordained routines, the staff over-reacted with harsh, punitive behaviors which triggers assault-provoking cycle.

Lanza and colleagues found that strict rules and limit setting leads to an extreme level of provocation, and that physically setting limits on patient behaviors caused many assaults, particularly among patients with organic brain syndrome or dementia.

The amount of conflict within the staff, between the staff and administration, and between the staff and the doctors all have a profound effect on the amount of agitation and assault in a facility

Emotional Climate

While environmental factors play an important part in the emotional state of the individual, milieu factors set the emotional tone for the *environment*. Simply stated, the more emotional conflict there is in a facility, the more assault will occur.

Under-staffing results in caregivers being over-worked. Consequently residents don't get the attention they need. While the staff becomes frazzled trying to meet the needs of everyone, the residents become agitated when needed help does not arrive. By the time the caregiver is able to attend to the resident, both are already in a high state of agitation.

Staff Conflict

The amount of conflict within the staff, between the staff and administration, and between the staff and the doctors all have a profound effect on the amount of agitation and assault in a facility. When a staff member is angry at a doctor or a superior, they may displace this anger unto the resident. This "kick the dog" behavior can result in a poor relationship between the caregiver and residents, and sets everyone on edge.

Psychological factors

The most potent predictor of assault is a *history of assault*. That is to say that the more often a person has been assaultive, the more likely it is that they will continue to be that way. When you are informed that a person has been assaultive, gather as much information as you can about the person's assault history. Find out how frequently the person has been violent, with whom, and under what circumstances. Give this information to all caregivers.

People with histories of assault and those with disorders that include loss of impulse control (like organic brain syndrome and borderline personality disorder) should be considered as high-risk, and need an immediate clinical evaluation for their assault potential. A plan of for prevention and management should be implemented as soon as the person arrives. All staff should be informed of these measures.

In one study of geropsychiatric state hospital patients in North Carolina, Colenda & Hamer reported that elder patients with schizophrenia or bipolar disorder committed 20.8 percent and 10.4 percent respectively of the assaultive behaviors on the unit.

In addition to having an increased personal space described above, people with schizophrenia tend to be especially sensitive to questions. Because they already have a fragile sense of self, questions are seen as intrusive and overwhelming. Many years ago one of my patients told me, "When you ask a question, it feels like a knife cutting my arm off." To this day, I remember that statement, and respectfully avoid questions.

As mentioned earlier, demented people also don't like questions. Questions often put them in an embarrassing position of trying to think or remember, and they react with anger in an effort to cover up their disability.

Physiological Factors

Despite the profound effect the environment has on those working and living in it, people differ in how their world affects them. What a person brings to a situation is as important as what the situation brings to the person.

Figure 1 illustrates that two people in the same

For people with memory impairments, the environment is always unfamiliar, which increases stress significantly

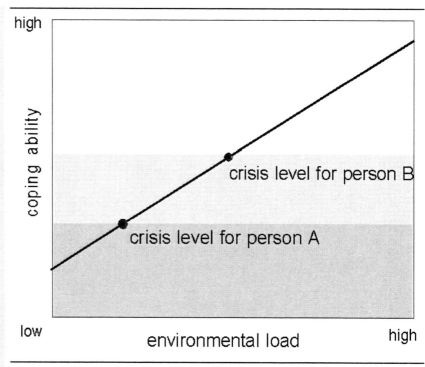

coping ability

crisis level for person B

crisis level for person A

low

environmental load

high

Figure 1 Coping and the environment

environment may have differing abilities to cope with environmental stress. But a person's normal level of coping skills may also depend on how that person is feeling physically.

Physical illnesses such as colds, flu, or infections lower a person's tolerance for frustration. We all get grumpy when we don't feel well, but in a cognitively challenged person, whose biochemistry is already askew, any illness or infection may cause delirium, confusion, and aggression. It's important to be aware that elderly people require a much longer time to recover from an illness, and their frustration tolerance may remain impaired for weeks. Medical toxicity may also trigger aggression. Drugs metabolize much slower in the elderly, and weakened livers and kidneys are unable to excrete toxins rapidly. For this reason many medications should be given in low doses to ascertain tolerance.

Drug reactions cause many incidents also. Some elders exhibit paradoxical reactions to drugs. For example recent studies show that rage reactions can occur in elderly patients who recently started taking benzodiazepines. Diazepam (Valium), especially when given in low doses, can cause extreme agitation and assaultive behavior. There have also reports of violent behavior occurring as reaction to various psychotropic drugs.

Dehydration can lead to electrolyte imbalances, confusion and aggression. Water balance decreases with age, in fact, body water level falls from 62 percent at age 25 to less than 50 percent at age 55. Older people may further restrict their water intake because of incontinence, and because they lose their sense of thirst.

Advertisers of laxatives often point out that "occasional irregularity" leads to irritability. While these ads are comical, they speak truth. Constipation can and does lead to uncomfortable feelings and makes people edgy, irritable, and unpleasant. High fiber diets can do wonders for a person plagued with this problem.

Sleep deprivation can also put a person on edge. In fact, chronic sleep problems can not only increase aggression but can lead to confusion and hallucinations.

Seizure disorders, especially temporal lobe seizures, can cause violent outbursts

Damage to the brain can have a noticeably effect on aggression. Seizure disorders, especially temporal lobe seizures, can cause violent outbursts. During a seizure, a person is capable of carrying out complex, goal directed violent behavior which they have no memory of after the incident. Several studies report that as many as one-half of temporal lobe epileptics experience aggressive behavior.

Brain damage to structures affecting perception and

inhibitory control, especially frontal and temporal lobes, results in *disinhibition*—the inability to control impulses.

Patients with *fronto-temporal dementia* are especially prone to aggressive behavior, and patients with this diagnosis should be approached with caution. A person with frontal lobe problems loses the capacity to make conscious decisions about the consequences of his actions. Instead, impulses are acted upon without thought of their outcome.

This means that even though a person who commits assault may feel remorse afterwards, their impaired impulse control may cause them to repeat the behavior. People with impulse control disorders do not learn from experience and behavioral interventions such as giving consequences and setting limits are often ineffective. In these cases, preventing the condition that led to the assault is the best intervention.

Those with cognitive impairment often misinterpret the actions of others, and may see caregiving activities as threats. They may also become reactive to being touched.

Elderly patients with dementia or schizophrenia may panic when caregivers approach

Elderly patients with dementia or schizophrenia may panic when caregivers approach. Jones (1985) reported that an aggressive response occurred most often when the patient could not understand the intentions of staff.

In fact, demented patients commit over 66 percent of the assaults on caregivers and other residents. The severity of dementia is related to the severity of assaultive behavior. For this reason, it's a good idea to inform the person what you are about to do, and ask permission before you begin.

Caregiver Factors

In studies of assaultive behavior in nursing homes, many incidents of assault occurred when two or three staff members approached a patient at one time. The team approach created a panic response from the patient —who felt attacked and invaded, and struggled to defend himself.

Sixty-five percent of assaults are against the nursing staff and nursing aides—the people who have the most frequent contact with residents. Unfortunately, they are also the least likely to have been trained to deal with aggression.

But even though assaults happen frequently, few patients behave aggressively in the absence of aversive stimulation. Whittington & Wykes investigated the frequency with which violence by psychiatric inpatients was preceded by a negative interpersonal encounter. *Out of 63 assaults, 86 percent were immediately preceded by the assaulted nurse having caused frustration in the patient, placed an unwanted activity demand on them, or engaged in some from of physical contact.*

Even more interesting is the finding by Baltes and associates that much of the care giving going on health care facilities was unnecessary.

Baltes noticed that when staff members are given a set of general care giving instructions, they tend to adhere to them regardless of the competence level of the resident. Thus many residents who were capable of self-care behaviors were treated in the same manner as those who were unable to help themselves. In fact, the studies indicated that in some facilities, *almost 80 percent of care-giving behaviors on the units were the result of compliance with staff instructions, rather than requests for help from the residents.* In addition, the residents stated that they were fully aware that they were not doing things that they were actually able to do.

All this adds up to a clear conclusion—most assault occurs during caregiving, and a great deal of care giving is unnecessary. It would seem then that the most effective solution is to assess the resident's ability to care for him or herself, and give them as much autonomy as possible. Intervene only when necessary.

Interpersonal Skills

Interpersonal factors play a significant role in assault and a poor relationship between a resident and a caregiver is a warning sign of trouble.

Caregivers that have personal problems with patients develop unhealthy relationships, which lead to disagreements, anger, and aggression.

A common problem I see is residents provoking the staff by making derogatory and racist remarks about them. It takes great skill and experience to shrug off this abuse.

Staff who are poorly trained and feel unable to control violence in some cases actually scare patient's into acting aggressively. Because they are unable to contain their own anxiety they escalate agitated patients.

It's also been found that staff members that were the most concerned about patient violence were those that feared they would not be able to contain their own violence if provoked.

The presence of male staff members increases assault. This is believed to be because of an assumption by residents that males are more threatening and provocative.

In addition, it's been noted that male staff tend to use confrontation as a means of resolving conflict, and that this method often increased agitation. Confrontation was found to be counterproductive in most episodes of agitation and assault.

Researchers Pauline Levy and Peter Hartocollis found that violence decreases in aggressive patients when the staff are female. They believe this is because female staff are less likely to act in an aggressive manner and because some patients perceive male staff as authority figures that threaten their sense of autonomy. In addition, many assaultive patients actually stated that they were less likely to hit a woman. Because of this, it's probably a good idea to have female staff initially intervene to de-escalate impending conflicts

System overload

As we have seen, people differ in their capacity to cope with environmental load. Individuals become aggressive when their socially sanctioned coping skills break down. For example, if a person cuts in front of you in a line, you may politely point it out to them. If they respond in an insulting manner, you might get angry. If they become belligerent, you might forget politeness and begin to act aggressively. All of us have a coping limit. As Mehrabian points out, *aggression occurs when the environmental load exceeds a person's ability to cope with it.*

For a cognitively impaired person, this coping limit can be very small. As we have seen, too much stimulation, unwanted activities, and violations of personal space are the most common causes of overload.

PREVENTING ASSAULT

1. If a person has a continuing negative reaction to a staff member, assign a new primary care giver.

2.Reinforce behavioral limits frequently.

3 Assess the person's need for personal space and privacy.

Allow ample space between you and the patient. Place personal items in their room, including furniture if possible.

4. When it has been determined that violation personal space causes fighting, stay out of the person's personal space.

Knock on their door before entering their room
Stay a few feet away and talk to them in a calm manner. Avoid interventions in a small room.

5. Provide appropriate opportunities for the person to be assertive instead of aggressive.

6. Give the person as much control as possible.

Autonomy and power lessen the need for aggression. The more control a person has in decisions pertaining to them, the more cooperative they become.

Prior to assaultive behaviors, most people display increased anger and agitation. The earlier you can identify and intervene in these emotions the less likely it is that an assault will occur. Agitation may be caused by many things, but as discussed earlier, it's usually a triggered by cognitive impairment combined with system overload.

Patients who are about to become assaultive often begin to pace in an agitated fashion and verbally express their irritation. Other behaviors include fist pounding, pressured speech, repeatedly requesting assistance from others and repetitive questioning.

PREVENTING ASSAULT

The first step in preventing assault is to get a thorough history of the person. An initial assessment should be informed immediately after a patient's admission to measure their assault potential. Find out if the person has a history of assault, of aggression, or general unpleasantness. Special precautions need to be taken when patients have a history of assault. If the person does have a history of violence, find out what precipitates it, and avoid these events when possible.

Become aware of the person's personal buffer zone, and inform all staff about it. Staff should always maintain personal space to promote feelings of security for the patient.

When the patient is not angry, limit-setting technique can be used to control verbally assaultive behavior. Setting limits the patient's behavior informs patients about what behavior is or is not acceptable. In addition, the leader will calmly describe the consequences of unacceptable behavior

BEHAVIORAL INTERVENTIONS FOR ASSAULT

Start simple

1. When fighting or assault occurs, separate the participants immediately

2. Remove all participants to a quiet room for time out

3. Tell the parties involved that the behavior is not acceptable, but do not scold or shame them.

4. Be respectful, call the person by name, express concern and ask how you can help

5. Ask the person who committed the assault why they did it

6. Determine whether their complaint was valid

Assault is never justified, but the event that led up to it may be a valid complaint. If the person has a valid compliant, explore constructive solutions to the problem.

7. If two people fight frequently, take steps to keep them separated. Re-assign rooms when necessary.

8. If a person cannot be managed without restrictive measures, the use of seclusion may be necessary to protect that individual and others.

It is also important to keep the other patients safe by removing them from the tense situation.

People with impulse control disorders do not learn from experience, and behavioral interventions such as giving consequences and setting limits are often ineffective.

9. Restraints should be used only as a last resort.

Studies show that in most cases restraints increase agitation. But if a person is out of control to the degree that they may harm themselves or others, restraints may be necessary. In these cases, the person should be told he is being restrained for his protection and safety.

10. After an assault, the staff should reassess the milieu.

The milieu needs to be non-threatening and calm in order to facilitate the assaultive patient's successful re-entry. The staff should explore the patient and caregiver factors that may have precipitated the assault, and take steps to prevent a reoccurrence.

Chapter twenty-two

WANDERING

Kirk: What could possibly be the purpose of this madness?
Spock: Madness has no purpose or reason, but it may have a goal.
    Star Trek, *Lazarus*

Behavioral Objectives

At the end of this section readers will be able to

Describe the causes of wandering

Discuss the definitions of wandering

Compare and contrast the benefits and risks of wandering

Provide opportunities for wandering in a safe enviornment

Remember the last time you entered a room only to realize you had no idea why you were there? Afer a moment of frozen confusion, you probably scanned the room, searching for a cue as to why you came. Not wanting to leave empty handed, you may have canvassed the area, examining everything, hoping to find the object that you came for.

Once you had looked everywhere, you threw your hands in the air in frustration, and returned empty handed to your starting place. To make things worse, as soon as you got back, you immediately remembered the purpose of your journey.

For most of us this happens infrequently, maybe once in a week or month, but for people with dementia or other cognitive problems, this experience is the norm.

A demented person's journey begin's just as yours did—with a clear purpose. But because their memory is

223

failing, the goal is quickly forgotten. Moments after the brain has sent the message to the motor system, the reason for the journey disappears. And because motor programs run without conscious awareness, the person will continue to walk long after he has forgotten why he departed.

Unlike you, however, a demented person has no way to recover the memory which prompted their journey. Returning to their place of origin doesn't work. In fact, they cannot remember their place of origin—they can't even recall where they were a moment ago. This lack of continuity causes them to experience a never ending series of desires without destinations.

We call this problem *wandering*—a common problem in the demented, and one which can be harmful to the person and to those around him.

In fact, wandering is often the most difficult behaviors to manage. Because of this, wanderers are often excluded from nursing homes because of the potential disruption, the disturbance of other residents, and the risk of injury.

The incidence of wandering

According to researchers Snyder and colleagues, there is one wanderer in every ten skilled nursing facility residents, and six in every 100 residents in intermediate level care facilities.

Among those living at home, hundreds of elderly people wander from their homes every day, and about 40% of them become lost when they wander. Fifteen percent of these people become lost for more than 6 hours, and the police become involved in one third of the cases. It's important to note that the average time between the first time a person gets lost from wandering and institutionalization is eight months.

The causes of wandering

Wandering has often been described as aimless movement—a behavior without an aim or a goal. However, even though wandering looks like purposeless behavior, it has meaning when viewed through the eyes of the wanderer.

A person who paces around a room randomly is drawn to various environmental cues—like dishes, clothing or personal items. They may in fact be acting quite purposefully, but as they pick up the first item, they forget their purpose. Each act becomes disrupted because of the inability to hold a goal in long-term memory. Even though these behaviors appear meaningless they are—for the moment—both purposeful and important. In fact, interference with the behavior of a wanderer often results in anger, agitation, and even catastrophic reactions.

I'm a morning person, but a few weeks ago I had to stay up late to finish a project. I woke the next morning in a fog, and staggered to my coffee pot. Semi-conscious, I scooped the grounds from the container, and poured them directly into my coffee cup.

Obviously this is not the result I was looking for. Although I have made coffee thousands of times, in my confused condition I had left out several important steps—putting the coffee in the pot, adding the water, and turning it on.

And this is just what happens in dementia. Motor programs are often left intact, but what is missing is the proper *sequencing* of these programs.

Like my fumbled attempt to make the morning

coffee, behaviors may be executed out of sequence. Without sequencing, the cognitively impaired person engages in what looks like a set of unconnected, random behaviors. Purposeful actions do occur, but the *plan* is missing. Actions occur at random, making the person's behavior appear confused and pointless.

Other reasons to wander

Even though much wandering is caused by these sequential confusions, there are other causes

Pain can cause anxiety and agitation. We all become more animated when we get agitated, and many of us pace when we are angry. For the cognitively impaired person, with little control over his life and poor problem solving skills, wandering may be the only outlet to work off this energy and it may be the only way they can express their discomfort.

And this may be an old habit. Researchers Monsour and Robb found that even before the onset of cognitive impairment, patients exhibiting wandering behavior had a history of relieving stress by physical means such as walking.

It has been suggested that wandering is sometimes a means of alleviating loneliness, and may be a substitute for social interaction. Cornbleth observed that regardless of a person's freedom of movement, the social interaction of the wanderers was much less than non-wanderers.

As people become more cognitively impaired, they spend more time alone than do the non-demented. Because they have difficulty carrying on a conversation, they are often excluded from social activities. For this reason, Cornbleth suggests that reducing wandering might be accomplished by increasing the opportunities for social interaction.

Wandering can also be triggered by environmental an emotional aspects of the milieu. Each patient has a biological drive for stimulation that includes the need for a certain amount of varied, meaningful activity.

Problems arise when the patient's drive for stimulation and the stimulation level in the facility don't match. A person can then be either over- or under-stimulated. The quantity and quality of environmental stimulation and the subsequent impact on sensory overload or deprivation contribute to the need to escape to a more comfortable place.

As spatial deficits increase, wandering increases. As a person becomes increasingly confused about his environment, he may begin a quest to find something or someone familiar. In this case, wandering results from the inability of the person to make sense of her environment

Wandering also has been associated with "sun-downing." This type of wandering appears to be associated with the onset of darkness and is caused by the person's loss of spatial orientation in the dark. People with dementia are less able to maintain orientation in space without visual scanning than normal individuals.

Medical conditions associated with wandering.

Several studies have found that lower blood pressure is related to more pacing. Low blood pressure can result in hypoxia, which is often accompanied by restlessness.

It's also been discovered that an increase in psychotropics usually equals more standing and pacing. Psychotropic medications have little effect on modifying problem behaviors such as agitation, and can actually promote wandering behaviors in some people.

Confusion can be caused by many drugs, including diuretics, sedatives, antihypertensives, analgesics, anti-anxiety drugs, and drugs that affect the gastrointestinal tract.

For example, diuretics can cause an electrolyte imbalance, reflected in a low potassium and/or sodium level, which results in gross confusion. A sedative given at bedtime is often metabolized slowly in an elderly person and produces morning grogginess and disorientation. And a patient who receives a sedative at bedtime may then be unable to find the bathroom in the middle of the night because of grogginess, resulting in incontinence.

The definition of wandering

In 1989, OBRA mandated that all nursing homes indicate in their MDS (minimum data set) if a resident is a wanderer. However, the exact definition of wandering was not made not clear.

And it *is* difficult to define wandering. As we have seen wandering actually refers to a variety of behaviors. In general it is a tendency to move about in a seemingly aimless or disoriented fashion, in pursuit of an indefinable or unobtainable goal. Wandering has also been defined as any change in a person's physical location which results in his/her inability to return to the point of origin. Others have defined it as extended periods of movement without a full awareness of one's behavior

The behavior may include following others around, imitating other's behavior, attempting to leave the facility, tampering with doors, windows or machinery, or entering other's rooms.

Snyder found that wanderers were in motion a higher percentage of time than non-wanderers. In fact, the wanderers were in motion a full 55% of the time. Wanderers also had more problems with recent and remote memory, orientation to time and place, ability to respond appropriately to a given conversation topic and overall psychosocial skills. Other studies have found a strong relationship between the frequency of wandering and severity of dementia. In people who have dementia and are mobile, those with the greatest cognitive impairment are more apt to wander. In fact, an analysis of wandering behavior showed that two components—cognitive impairment and hyperactivity—differentiated wanderers from non-wanderers.

Thomas has studied the continuity of personality to wandering, and found that there were two general types of wanderers: *continuous wanderers* who wander more than 50% of the time, and *sporadic wanderers* who roam intermittently and in bursts of time. He suggests that the first step in intervening with wanderers is to ascertain whether they are continuous or sporadic.

Hussain has developed another way to define wanderers. He identified four types of wandering.

Exit seekers are those who repeatedly attempt to leave their physical environment. Wanderers attempting to exit the building will generally tell you that they are looking for someone or something, or that they need to go somewhere. For example, they may be obsessed with returning home, because they cannot remember why they are not there. This type of wandering may also be a remnant of a previous work role, or an attempt by the person to put some meaning and purpose into their life.

Akathesiacs are those who exhibit restlessness and pacing behavior. This is often the result of prolonged use of psychotropic medications. But other drugs may also cause restlessness. For example, certain people ave a paradoxical reaction to opiate based pain-killers (like codiene), and rather than sedating the person, they make him restless. Acetaminophen or non-steroidal anti-inflammatory drugs (NSAIDs) helps akathesiacs .

Self-stimulators are those whose focus is the desire to turn the knob on a door. They do not care necessarily about actually leaving, but instead want the physical stimulation of opening the door. Others may wander out of the need for sensory stimulation—wandering gives them something to do. These residents may wander down a hallway, touching everything repeatedly. This type of wandering is often a sign of under-stimulation or lack of structure.

The last type of wanderer is the *modeler.* Their focus is to follow those around them.. Because of cognitive deterioration, they get caught up in following someone else. This is a type of *echopraxia,* the involuntary mimicking of another's behavior. If the people they are with leave, they too want to leave

The Benefits of wandering

Within a safe environment, wandering can be beneficial. Wandering stimulates circulation and oxygenation, promotes exercise, and decreases contractures. Consequently, one of the goals of managing the wandering patient is providing a safe level of wandering without putting the patient at risk for injury.

Wandering stimulates circulation and promotes

beneficial muscle activity and oxygenation of the cells. It is also a way to channel excess energy and anxiety.

As mentioned above wandering is a way for the person to cope with stress and find security. Overall, wandering is viewed as having a beneficial effect for the wanderer by fulfilling a particular need.

The hazards of wandering

Despite its potential benefits, wandering is often associated with negative outcomes for both the wanderer and caregiver.

Researchers have categorized problems caused by wandering as either *safety* or *nuisance* related, the most significant safety problem being a wanderer's attempts to leave the facility.

Unless a facility is locked, people suffering from dementia or other forms of confusion frequently attempt to leave the facility and may place themselves in peril. According to Burnside, approximately 20% of the staff members at long-term care facilities have reported at least one incident where wandering resulted in serious injury or death.

A number of factors may prompt wanderers to exit through doors. Some are attracted to the view outside the door or light at the door, both which enhance the attractiveness of leaving the unit. Others may be cued to attempt exiting behavior by the protrusion of a door knob or may be attracted to the shininess of the bar on the door, which may cause residents to touch the door and trigger the alarm, even when they did not intend to exit.

But besides the danger, this behavior is also disruptive to other residents and to caregivers, as wanderers frequently intrude into other people's rooms, hop into their beds, or rummage through their belongings.

Persistent wandering eventually takes its emotional toll on those involved—both patients and caregivers. As staff members attempts various creative ways to restrict wandering, the patients often become more agitated, restless and determined. The caregivers often become frustrated as they try to protect the patient from falls and other adverse effects of the incessant and seemingly aimless activity. This frustration sometimes leads to counterproductive methods such as physical or chemical restraint, which can actually increase agitation and injury.

Many nursing homes have established special care units designed to accommodate wanderers. However, since most facilities were not originally created for dementia patients, they place the wanderer into an environment that is not suited for their needs.

BEHAVIORAL INTERVENTIONS FOR WANDERING

Remember that even though wandering may pose a safety risk to the patient, there are beneficial effects of wandering. Intervention should focus on understanding why the behavior is present, and if it seems to be therapeutic, allowing it to continue at a controlled and safe level.

The use of physical and chemical restraints should not be used, as they tend to promote agitation and injury and do little to reduce falls.

1. Approach the person from the side or from the front and gently redirect her away from exits and other resident's rooms.

Walk her back to the common area. If you know this person will not react negatively to being touched, take her by the hand or elbow, and walk her in the desired direction.

2. While you are guiding them back, distract them by talking about something they like.

You can also re-focus them by handing them an object, such as a stuffed toy. By focusing attention on some object such as a toy, a set of keys or a wristwatch, patients forget that they were attempting to leave. Another means of diversion is providing patients with activities such as organizing magazines.

3. Remember that the behavior that the person is engaged in may be based on a delusion.

This type of behavior is usually of short duration. In these instances it is sometimes best to allow the resident to finish what they are doing before redirecting them. If so,

5. Comment on what you think the person may be trying to do, and what they are feeling.

If they say, "I've got to get back to work," address the feeling by saying, "I know that work is important to you," while you redirect them.

6. Use verbal commands that focus on what you would like the person to do, rather than what she should not do.

It is much harder to understand the command, "Don't go out there" than the simpler command, "Stay in the building." This is because telling a demented person not to do something requires *inhibition*, while telling him to

Wandering checklist:

Has the person's amount of social interaction decreased?

Does the patient have a history of relieving stress by physical means?

Does this person have a history of the wandering behavior?

Can this person find the bathroom unassisted?

What time of day is the wandering most prevalent?

What type of wandering is usually exhibited?

Does the person return after he wanders?

Does wandering increase after family visits?

do something prompts them to action.

7. Always look around before exiting the area.

8. Use visual barriers and disguises

Doorknobs and push bars are cues for the hand to reach, even when the person does not intend to leave the unit. A beige cloth secured across the doorway with Velcro will hide the doorknob, and stop this problem.

Another visual barrier that has worked well consists of a painted grid on the floor in front of doorways. Capitalizing on cognitive deficits, the grid gives the appearance of an unstable surface, and the patient refuses to walk near the door.

Since many wanderers perceive breaks in carpet patterns or tiles as dangerous holes, place a mat or use a different pattern of carpet in front of exits.

9. Use wander-guards when appropriate.

Electronic monitoring of the patients by the use of patient monitoring arm bands and electronic monitoring devices at selected doorways have been used in some facilities. Similar to department store security systems, an alarm is activated when a patient goes through the doorway. This intervention serves more to help the nursing staff know where the patients are than to act as a deterrent to inhibiting the movements of the patients .

10. Use large name and address tags.

The tag will help people return the wanderer home. If possible, inform the local police of wanderers.

11. Keep outdoor clothing such as hats and overcoats out of sight.

These items often act as triggers to begin wandering behavior.

12. Schedule a time period when they are encouraged to walk and engage in other physical activity.

Provide a wide variety of short-term, structured activities to reduce anxiety and help the person feel they are spending their time in a constructive, meaningful way.

13. Gather all the wandering patients together, and take them for a walk.

This will accomplish several things. First, it will remove them from the environment where they may be disrupting others. Second, it will allow them to do what they are already doing, but the behavior now becomes prescribed and structured. Third, it will increase their quality of life. Fourth, it will allow them to expend energy so that they are less agitated at other times. Finally, daily exercise will improve their sleep.

14. Make sure that the person has access to windows

Windows allow the person to view the environment and keep an awareness of the weather, season, and time of day. Windows also expose the person to light, which helps regulate their biological clock. These improves sleep and reduces nocturnal wandering.

15. Make sure the person has eye-glasses and hearing aids if they need them.

Loss of vision and hearing can result in decreased stimulation, and lead to wandering as a stimulus-seeking behavior.

16. Use behavior modification

In a recent experiment food rewards such as applesauce. chocolate, candies, or a sip of cola–were used as the primary reinforcer for desired behavior. A loud hand clap near the patient's ear served as an aversive stimulus. In 3-minute training sessions, a reward was given to the patient in the presence of a large orange rectangle, and the hand clap was administered while the patient was looking at a blue circle. The orange rectangle became associated with good times ahead while the blue circle was associated with an unpleasant experience.

The orange card was then posted in places that were safe to wander—such as the patient's room, the lounge and the hall, while blue circles were posted near hazards like staircases closets, or exits. This decreased wandering significantly.

In one special care facility for dementia patients, several patients were former POWs of World War II. They often attempted to escape by climbing over the walls surrounding the outdoor area of the facility. When an "OFF LIMITS" sign, which was commonly used in the military, was put on the wall, there were no further attempts to escape.

In another facility, a men's club was held two evenings a week, which resulted in calming its members. Folding clothes, gardening, supervised walks, or cooking activities provide social contact. Helping residents participate in activities in which they have a high chance to succeed decreasing the desire to leave.

17. Monitor the person frequently to insure that all physiological needs are being met.

A person who is hungry, uncomfortable or in pain is more prone to wander. Usually when a resident wanders into another resident's room it is because he is in search of a bathroom.

18. Decrease Nighttime wandering

For nighttime wanderers, environmental factors associated with nocturnal wandering such as excessive background noise should be reduced, so make sure that the room is quiet and comfortable.

Providing a steady background noise such as a ticking clock, an aquarium pump, or headphones with relaxation tapes or special music can also help keep residents calm and in their rooms at night. The use of 'white noise' also reduces nocturnal wandering and promotes sounder sleep. White noise can be any low intensity, continuous, rhythmic sound such as a window fan.

Establish a bed time routine and put physical activities in the afternoon Toilet the resident before bedtime and frequently throughout the night. Many times a confused resident attempts to crawl out of bed and wander because he is wet or his bladder is full.

Chapter twenty-three
GROUPS

Regardless of a person's age, she may be grossly immature in certain facets of her life. Like younger people, many elderly people lack coping skills, communication skills, problem solving skills, and a solid sense of self-worth.

We often attribute these problems to old age, when in fact they have existed throughout the person's entire life. The grumpy and abusive old man in room 3 may actually be that way because he never learned a better way to communicate. Old people do not automatically get grumpy, but grumpy people do get old. Groups can be an effective way to correct these deficits.

However, many elderly people are reluctant to participate, or to be self disclosing in groups. Where a younger person may be more eager to connect, elderly people often state that they have no interest in bonding with anyone. They fear that getting to know other people on an intimate basis will result in further loss. This must be kept in mind when examining resistance to care and group participation.

People with cognitive problems may find groups

Behavioral Objectives

At the end of this section readers will be able to

Discuss the goals of group activity

Explain the reluctance to participate in group activity

List the common types of groups and their purposes

Use tools to conduct successful groups

confusing and overwhelming. For his reason each potential group member should be screened to see if they may benefit from group experience.

GROUP GOALS

The immediate goals of group participation are

1. To improve the person's self esteem through many success-oriented interactive experiences.

2. To improve the person's ability to talk about thoughts, feelings, fantasies and ideas in the presence of others.

3. To foster concern and caring for oneself.

4. To teach empathy and demonstrate concern for others

5. To maximize the ability for the person to express themselves within their limitations.

6. To learn to listen and to respond, not react.

7. To provide a supportive, non-critical environment in which to express fears, losses, anxieties, and problems.

8. To provide social stimulation.

9. To teach problem solving and planning skills.

10. To help members become more responsible for themselves.

11. To maximize autonomy.

12. To learn how to problem solve in socially

appropriate ways.

13. To develop an awareness of the consequences of one's actions.

14. To integrate one's self to society with feelings of being worthwhile and loveable.

15. To develop the awareness that many people share similar fears, anxieties and disturbing thoughts.

TYPES OF GROUPS

Assertiveness Training

The purpose of assertiveness training is to learn the differences between non-assertive, assertive and aggressive behavior, to become aware of the ways that people are manipulated, coerced, or made to feel guilty by others, and to learn, practice and develop assertive behaviors.

Communication Skills

The purpose of a communication skills group is to explain the differences between effective and ineffective communication, to learn to recognize the barriers to com-munication, and to teach specific listening and expressive skills.

Specific skills include:

Writing down the problem to be solved.

Discussing only one issue at a time.

Staying focused on solving the problem rather than winning the argument.

Making statements instead of asking questions.

Popular songs

1901 Chocolate Creams
     Cake Walk
1902 Bill Bailey, Won't You
     Please Come Home
1903 St. Louis Rag, Ida
     (Sweet As Apple Cider)
1904 Red Devil Rag,
     The St. Louis Tickle
1905 My Gal Sal
1906 Dill Pickles Rag
1907 Kansas City Rag
1908 Memphis Rag
1909 Put on your Old Gray
     Bonnett
1910 Steamboat Bill
1911 Alexander's Ragtime
     Band,
     My Melancholy Baby
1912 Memphis Blues,
     Look For The Silver
     Lining
1913 Peg O' My Heart,
     You Made Me Love You
1914 St. Louis Blues
1915 Jelly Roll Blues
     I Ain't Got Nobody
1916 Pretty Baby
1917 Darktown Strutters Ball
     Tiger Rag
1918 Ja Da
     Oh How I Hate To Get
     Up In The Morning
1919 Swanee,
     Baby, Won't You
     Please Come Home
1920 You Can't Keep a Good
     Man Down
1921 I'm Just Wild About
     Harry
     April Showers
1922 My Honey's Lovin'
     Arms
     Chicago
1923 Charleston
1924 Tea For Two
     The Man I Love
1925 Sweet Georgia Brown
     Muskrat amble

Being assertive, not abusive.

Emotional Education

The purpose of emotional education group is to teach the group members about the eight primary emotions, to recognize their own emotional reactions to specific situations, and to learn ways for controlling or coping with their emotional reactions. Group members are educated in recognizing the basic emotions and labeling them when they occur. They are also taught when it is appropriate to express these emotions, and how to express them clearly and constructively.

Depression Group

The purpose of this group is to help people recognize the symptoms of depression, so that they can identify depression in themselves and others. It's useful to give each person a symptom sheet, so that they can review it later. Members also should be shown how depression causes cognitive distortions, and the loss of pleasure in life. Each group should contain a section in which the group members share their feelings, and other members offer solutions to the problems expressed.

Motivation Groups

This group encourages people to share various kinds of information about activities and pleasant social experiences. The purpose is to motivate people to interact socially and establish a richer environment through the discussion of concrete and specific topics such as vacations, gardening, pets, art, hobbies, and nature. Because these groups are a way to recapture pleasure, motivation groups work well in conjunction with depression groups.

Music Therapy

Music therapy helps people in several ways. First, music is a structured, rhythmic event that stimulates the senses, the emotions, and the body which provokes a response from the individual. Second, it provide a means of self-expression, allowing the person to communicate his moods, feelings for others, and attitudes about life on a nonverbal level.

Third, it facilitates interpersonal relationships and social interactions—dancing and singing has always brought people together. Fourth, music is a powerful way to evoke memory and stimulate thought. Everyone has a favorite song, or has special memories that are tied to music.

In the margins are a few popular songs from past eras.

Medication Groups

Medication groups educate people about the effects and side-effects of medications. This group also includes information about good and bad drugs, over-the counter-drugs, and the effects of various herbs, vitamins, and nutrients. The group should also teach members about the hazards of abuse, medication compliance, and methods of medication administration (e.g. pill boxes, oral and injections).

Reminiscence Groups

This group permits the exchange of early experience of many sorts, such as holiday celebrations and cooking favorite foods. It promotes interpersonal relationships and a sense of belonging, stimulates thought processes, and brings back pleasant memories.

1927 Old Man River
Blue Skies
1928 You Do Something To Me
I'll Get By
1929 Honeysuckle Rose
Am I Blue
1930 I Got Rhythm
Rockin' Chair
1931 All of Me, Lazy River
1932 It Don't Mean A Thing;
1933 Don't Blame Me
I've Got the World on a String
1934 Stompin' at the Savoy
1935 Porgy And Bess
Blue Moon
1936 I've Got You Under My Skin
1937 I've Got My Love To Keep Me Warm
1938 My Heart Belongs To Daddy
1939 Somewhere Over The Rainbow
1940 Fools Rush In
1941 How About You
I Got It Bad (And That Ain't Good)
1942 White Christmas
That Old Black Magic
1943 As Time Goes By
1944 Have Yourself A merry Little Christmas
1945 Anything You Can Do, Deep Purple
1947 How Are Things in Gloccamora
1948 Buttons And Bows
1949 Scarlet Ribbons
1950 On A Clear Day You Can See Forever
1953 I Love Paris
1954 Misty
1955 Blue Lights
1958 Satin Doll

Sensory Training Group

The purpose of this group is to increase function or prevent further deterioration of cognitively impaired people by providing many types of stimuli that arouse the person's senses, promote awareness and elicit meaningful responses.

Orientation Groups

To supplement daily reorientation, the person is taken to a special class in Reality Orientation which lasts for approximately 30 minutes and varies in size from two to eight residents. During these classes, the person is given basic information and is helped to relearn it by making new associations with words, pictures and objects.

Horticulture Groups

For many people, tending plants is reason for getting out of bed. This is a motivation that many people need. People who have a plant to care for report more satisfaction in long term care facilities.

Art Therapy

For many older individuals, art can providing an enjoyable, meaningful life experience. This is especially true after the person has an opportunity to work with the various forms of art. These can include painting, drawing, sculpting, pottery and crafts.

Movement Therapy

The goals of this group include: Release of tension: reduction of anxiety; re-socialization through group interaction and shared movement experiences; improvement of body image, and sense of self-worth, and self-confidence in one's own body actions; stimulation of verbalization; and physical conditioning and exercise.

Recreation Therapy

A way of helping residents direct their attention away from their illnesses toward healthy leisure activity is through some form of recreation. Recreation motivates and re-awakens in the resident an interest in things that are fun and encourage the healing process.

Exercise Groups

Constructive physical activity is vital for an individual's well being. An exercise program will delay the slowing down process of the body, contribute to self esteem, and stabilize mood.

This program encourages the use of appropriate recreational facilities in the community. Daily recreational therapy sessions may include physical therapy, dance therapy, music therapy, art therapy and a variety of crafts. Crafts include ceramics, wood projects, leather tooling, needle crafting and various other crafts.

Family Support Groups

A family support group is a vital and valuable service offered to the families and friends of the elderly patient. The purpose of the group is to allow open expression of feelings that the family member/friend may be experiencing in their relationship with the patient. The support group also allows the family member/friend the opportunity to problem solve issues relating to physical, financial, social, and environmental concerns.

In addition, the support group leader teaches members about the origins and reasons for the problems and difficulties their loved ones are experiencing.

REFERENCES

1. AGEISM

Adams T. The case for breaking through ageism in mental health care. *Nursing Times*, 1996 Mar 20- 26, 92(12):46-7.

Adams T. Working in partnership to end ageism in mental health. *British Journal of Nursing*, 1997 Feb 13-26, 6(3):133.

Coontz, S. *The way we never were* Basic Books, NY., 1992

Fuller D. Challenging ageism through our speech. *Nursing Times*, 1995 May 24-30, 91(21):29- 31.

Goulden, Joseph *The Best Years* Athenuem, NY., 1976

Haight BK; Christ MA; Dias JK. Does nursing education promote ageism? *Journal of Advanced Nursing*, 1994 Aug, 20(2):382-90.

James JW; Haley WE. Age and health bias in practicing clinical psychologists. *Psychology and Aging*, 1995 Dec, 10(4):610-6.

Lash, C. *The Culture of Narcissism* W.W. Norton, NY., 1978

McMinn B. Ageism: the challenge for nursing. *Australian Nursing Journal*, 1996 May, 3(10):18-21.

Ryan A. Focus on ageism [news]. *Elderly Care*, 1997 Feb-Mar, 9(1):40.

Seymour M. Putting an end to ageism. *Canadian Nurse*, 1994 Nov, 90(10):49-50.

2: LEAVING HOME

Cummings, E. & Henry, W (1961) *Growing Old: The Process of Disengagement* Basic Books, NY.

Havinghurst R. (1961) Successful aging *The Gerontologist* 1:8-13.

Coffman, S. and Coffman, V. (1986) Aging awareness training for professionals who work with the elderly. *Small Group Behavior*, 95-103.

Coffman TL. (1981) Relocation and survival of institutionalized aged: A re-examination of the evidence. *The Gerontologist* 21(5):483-500.

3: FAMILIES

Grafstrom M; Fratiglioni L; Sandman PO; Winblad B. Health and social consequences for relatives of demented and non-demented elderly. A population-based study. *Journal of Clinical Epidemiology*, 1992 Aug, 45(8):861-70.

Howe, G.W. (1994) Neurological trauma and family functioning: toward a social neuropsychology [comment] *Psychiatry* 57(3):275-7 Comment on: *Psychiatry* 1994 Aug;57(3):269-74.

4: MEMORY PROBLEMS

Allain H; Raoul P; Lieury A; LeCoz F; Gandon JM; d'Arbigny P. Effect of two doses of ginkgo biloba extract (EGb 761) on the dual-coding test in elderly subjects. *Clinical Therapeutics,* 1993 May-Jun, 15(3):549-58.

Erber JT; Szuchman LT. Memory performance in relation to age, verbal ability, and activity. *Experi-mental Aging Research,* 1996 Jan-Mar, 22(1): 59-72.

Cone, William *Stop Memory Loss! How to Fight Forgetfulness over Forty* Matteson Books, Pacific Palisades, CA .,1997.

Sandman, Curt A. Memory rehabilitation in Alzheimer's disease: Preliminary findings. Clinical *Gerontologist,* 1993, v13 (n4):19-33.

5. CONFUSION

Kroeger, L. L. [1991]. Critical care nurses' perceptions of the confused elderly patient, *Focus on Critical Care,* 18(5). 395.

Schor. J. D., Levkoll, S. E.. el al. (1992). Risk factors for delirium In hospitalized elderly. *JAMA.* 267(6), 27.

Levkofl. 5. E.. Evans. O. A., er al, (1992]. Delirium: The occurrence and persistence of symptoms among elderly hospitalized patients. *Arch. Intern. Med.* 152:21-33.

SunderlJiid, T. (1990). Organic brain disorders. In *The Merck manual of geriatrics.*

Evans. L. (1987). Sundown syndrome in insti- tutionalized elderly. *Am. Geriat. Soc.,* 35(5), 101.

Yeaw EM; Abbate JH. Identification of confusion among the elderly in an acute care setting. *Clinical Nurse Specialist,* 1993 Jul, 7(4):192-7.

Patkar AA; Kunkel EJ. Treating delirium among elderly patients. *Psychiatric Services,* 1997 Jan, 48(1):46-8.

Edmands MS. "Murder!" she said: a case of iatrogenic delirium. *Issues in Mental Health Nursing,* 1995 Mar-Apr, 16(2):109-16.

Warshaw G; Tanzer F. The effectiveness of lumbar puncture in the evaluation of delirium and fever in the hospitalized elderly. *Archives of Family Medicine,* 1993 Mar, 2(3):293-7.

Ostenveil D, Svndulko K, Cohen SN, et al: Cognitive function In non-demented older adults with hypothyroidism. *Journal of the American Geriatrics Society* 1992 ;40(4): 325-335

Touks C, Mental illness in hypothyroid patients *British Journal of Psychiatry* 1964;110:706-710

Whybrow PC, Prange J, Treadway CR, Mental changes accompanying thyroid gland dysfunction. *Archives of General Psychiatry* 1969;20:48-63

War DJ, Pastel ML: Prognosis in myxedematous madness. *British Journal of Psychiatry* 1967; 113:149-151

Haupt.C, Kurz, A Reversibiliry of dementia in hypothyroidism *Journal of Neurology* 240 :333 -335.

6. DEMENTIA

Postoff, R., Collins, A. and Eastwood, M. (1991) *Alzheimer's Disease and Related Disorders.* Toronto: Clarke Institute of Psychiatry.

Burdz,. M, Eaton,. W, Bond, J. (1988) Effect of respite care on dementia and non dementia patients and their caregivers. *Psychol of Aging* 3:38- 42.

Clendaniel, BP & Fleishell, A. (1979) An Alzheimer's day-care center for nursing horns patients. *American Journal of Nursing* 1075:944 -945

Geiser. R., Hoche. L., King. J. (1988) Respite care for mentally ill patients and their families. *Hospital Community Psychiatry* 39:291-295.

Funkenstein HH, Hicks R, Dysken MW, et al: Drug treatment of cognitive impairment in Alzheimer's disease and the late-life dementias, in *Clinical Aspects of Alzheimer's Disease and Senile Dementia*. Edited by Miller NE, Cohen GD. New York, Raven Press, 1981.

Thal LJ, Masur DM, Fuld PA, et al. (1983) Memory improvement with oral physostigmine and lecithin in Alzheimer's disease, in *Biological Aspects of Alzheimer's Disease*, Banbury Report 15. Edited by Katzman R. Cold Spring Harbor, NY, Cold Spring Harbor Laboratory.

Reisberg B, Ferris SH, Arnand R, et al: (1983) Effects of naloxone in senile dementia: a double -blind trial (ltr). *New England Journal of Medicine* 308:721-722.

Fact Sheet: Senile Dementia & Alzheimer's Disease. DHEW pub ADM 80-929. Rockville, MD National institute of Mental Health, 1980.

Alzheimer's Disease: A Scientific Guide for Health Practitioners, NIH Pub 81-2251. Bethesda, MD, National Institute of Health, 1980 Roth M: The psychiatric disorders of later life. *Psychiatric Annals* 6:57-101, 1976

Borell L; Sandman PO; Winblad B. Abilities and activities of patients with dementia in day hos-

pitals. *Scandinavian Journal of Caring Sciences,* 1991, 5(1):49-55.

Bucht G; Sandman PO. Nutritional aspects of dementia, especially Alzheimer's disease. *Age and Ageing*, 1990 Jul, 19(4):S32-6.

Carlson DL; Fleming KC; Smith GE; Evans JM. Management of dementia-related behavioral disturbances: a nonpharmacologic approach. *Mayo Clinic Proceedings*, 1995 Nov, 70(11): 1108-15.

Forsell Y; Jorm AF; Winblad B. Variation in psychiatric and behavioural symptoms at different stages of dementia: data from physicians' examinations and informants' reports. *Dementia,* 1993 Sep-Oct, 4(5):282-6.

Gugel RN. Behavioral approaches for managing patients with Alzheimer's disease and related disorders. *Medical Clinics of North America*, 1994 Jul, 78(4):861-7.

Karzman R (ed): *Biological Aspects of Alzheimer's Disease*, Banbury Report 15. Cold Spring Harbor, NY, Cold Spring Harbor Laboratory, 1983.

Katzman R. Terry RD, Bick K (eds): *Senile Dementia and Related Disorders*. New York, Raven Press, 1978.

Keene JM; Hope T. Hyperphagia in dementia: 1. The use of an objective and reliable method for measuring hyperphagia in people with dementia. *Appetite,* 1997 Apr, 28(2):151-65.

Mace NL, Rabins, PV *The 36-Hour Day.* Baltimore, Johns Hopkins University Press.

Miller NE, Cohen GD (eds): *Clinical Aspects of Alzheimer's Disease and Senile Dementia.* New York, Raven Press, 1981.

Peisah C; Brodaty H. Practical guidelines for the treatment of behavioural complications of dementia. *Medical Journal of Australia*, 1994 Nov 7, 161(9):558-63.

Sandman PO. Is good care the best treatment for the Alzheimer patient? *Acta Neurologica Scandinavica. Supplementum*, 1990, 129:37-9.

Smith-Jones, SM & Francis, GM (1992) Disruptive, Institutionalized Elderly: Cost Effective Intervention *Journal of Psychosocial Nursing* 30(10): 17-20.

7. DEPRESSION

Grimby A. Bereavement among elderly people: grief reactions, post-bereavement hallucinations and quality of life. *Acta Psychiatrica Scandinavica*, 1993 Jan, 87(1):72-80.

Lee MA; Ganzini L. Depression in the elderly: effect on patient attitudes toward life-sustaining therapy [see comments]. *Journal of the American Geriatrics Society*, 1992 Oct, 40(10):983-8.

Bell IR; Edman JS; Morrow FD; Marby DW; Perrone G; Kayne HL; Greenwald M; Cole JO. Brief communication. Vitamin B_1, B_2, and B_6 augmentation of tricyclic antidepressant treatment in geriatric depression with cognitive dysfunction. *Journal of the American College of Nutrition*, 1992 Apr, 11(2):159-63.

Conn DK; Goldman Z. Pattern of use of antidepressants in long-term care facilities for the elderly. *Journal of Geriatric Psychiatry and Neurology*, 1992 Oct-Dec, 5(4):228-32.

Brodaty H. Think of depression--atypical presentations in the elderly. *Australian Family Physician*, 1993 Jul, 22(7):1195-203.

Devanand DP; Nobler MS; Singer T; Kiersky JE; Turret N; Roose SP; Sackeim HA. Is dysthymia a different disorder in the elderly? *American Journal of Psychiatry*, 1994 Nov, 151(11):1592-9.

Prigerson HG; Frank E; Kasl SV; Reynolds CF 3rd; Anderson B; Zubenko GS; Houck PR; George CJ; Kupfer DJ. Complicated grief and bereavement-related depression as distinct disorders: preliminary empirical validation in elderly bereaved spouses. *American Journal of Psychiatry*, 1995 Jan, 152(1):22-30.

Reynolds CF 3rd. Recognition and differentiation of elderly depression in the clinical setting. *Geriatrics*, 1995 Oct, 50 Suppl 1:S6-15.

Alexopoulos GS; Vrontou C; Kakuma T; Meyers BS; Young RC; Klausner E; Clarkin J. Disability in geriatric depression. *American Journal of Psychiatry*, 1996 Jul, 153(7):877-85.

Rothschild AJ. The diagnosis and treatment of late-life depression. *Journal of Clinical Psychiatry*, 1996, 57 Suppl 5:5-11.

8. SUICIDE

Bron B. [Depression and suicide in the elderly]. *Zeitschrift fur Gerontologie*, 1992 Jan-Feb, 25(1): 43-52.

Canetto SS. Gender and suicide in the elderly. *Suicide and Life-Threatening Behavior*, 1992 Spring, 22(1):80-97.

Casey DA. Suicide in the elderly. *Journal of the Kentucky Medical Association*, 1990 Jun, 88(6): 301.

Casey DA. Suicide in the elderly: a two-year study of data from death certificates [see comments]. *Southern Medical Journal,* 1991 Oct, 84(10): 1185-7.

Conwell Y. Suicide in the elderly [see comments]. *Crisis*, 1992, 13(1):6-8.

De Leo D; Ormskerk SC. Suicide in the elderly: general characteristics. *Crisis,* 1991 Sep, 12(2):

3-17.

Drion H. Suicide in the elderly [letter; comment] [see comments]. *Crisis*, 1992, 13(2):52.

Duffy D. Suicide in later life: how to spot the risk factors. *Nursing Times*, 1997 Mar 12-18, 93(11): 56-7.

Galanos, AN. Suicide in the elderly [letter; comment]. *Southern Medical Journal*, 1992 Mar, 85(3):331.

Heiss HW. [Restriction or fulfillment. Ethical topics on suicide and sexuality of the elderly]. *Wiener Medizinische Wochenschrift*, 1992, 142 (23-24): 1 p. following 538.

Humphry D. Rational suicide among the elderly. *Suicide and Life-Threatening Behavior*, 1992 Spring, 22(1):125-9.

Horton-Deutsch SL; Clark DC; Farran CJ. Chronic dyspnea and suicide in elderly men. *Hospital and Community Psychiatry*, 1992 Dec, 43(12):1198-203.

Hochbaum GM. Suicide by the elderly [letter; comment]. *American Journal of Public Health*, 1992 Aug, 82(8):1175.

Kua EH; Ko SM. A cross-cultural study of suicide among the elderly in Singapore. *British Journal of Psychiatry*, 1992 Apr, 160:558-9.

Kerkhof A; de Leo D. Suicide in the elderly: a frightful awareness. *Crisis*, 1991 Sep, 12(2):81-7.

Lester D; Yang B. Social and economic correlates of the elderly suicide rate. *Suicide and Life-Threatening Behavior*, 1992 Spring, 22(1):36-47.

Loebel JP; Loebel JS; Dager SR; Centerwall BS; Reay DT. Anticipation of nursing home placement may be a precipitant of suicide among the elderly.

Journal of the American Geriatrics Society, 1991 Apr, 39(4):407-8.

Lyness JM; Conwell Y; Nelson JC. Suicide attempts in elderly psychiatric inpatients. *Journal of the American Geriatrics Society*, 1992 Apr, 40(4): 320-4.

McIntosh JL. Epidemiology of suicide in the elderly. *Suicide and Life-Threatening Behavior,* 1992 Spring, 22(1):15-35.

Mellick E; Buckwalter KC; Stolley JM. Suicide among elderly white men: development of a profile. *Journal of Psychosocial Nursing and Mental Health Services*, 1992 Feb, 30(2):29-34.

Nieto E; Vieta E; Lazaro L; Gasto C; Cirera E. Serious suicide attempts in the elderly. *Psychopathology*, 1992, 25(4):183-8.

Rifai AH; Reynolds CF; Mann JJ. Biology of elderly suicide. *Suicide and Life-Threatening Behavior*, 1992 Spring, 22(1):48-61.

Rao AV. Suicide in the elderly: a report from India. *Crisis,* 1991 Sep, 12(2):33-9.

Schmid H; Manjee K; Shah T. On the distinction of suicide ideation versus attempt in elderly psych-iatric inpatients. *Gerontologist*, 1994 Jun, 34(3): 332-9.

Skoog I; Aevarsson O; Beskow J; Larsson L; Palsson S; Waern M; Landahl S; Ostling S. Suicidal feelings in a population sample of non-demented 85-year-olds. *American Journal of Psychiatry,* 1996 Aug, 153(8):1015-20.

Sverre JM. Trends in suicide mortality among the elderly in Norway, 1966-1986. *Epidemiology,* 1991 Jul, 2(4):252-6.

Tatai K; Tatai K. Suicide in the elderly: a report from Japan. *Crisis,* 1991 Sep, 12(2):40-3.

9. ANXIETY

Martin LM; Fleming KC; Evans JM. Recognition and management of anxiety and depression in elderly patients [see comments]. *Mayo Clinic Proceedings*, 1995 Oct, 70(10):999- 1006.

Sheikh JI; Salzman C. Anxiety in the elderly. Course and treatment. *Psychiatric Clinics of North America*, 1995 Dec, 18(4):871-83.

Schneider LS. Overview of generalized anxiety disorder in the elderly. *Journal of Clinical Psychiatry*, 1996, 57 Suppl 7:34-45; discussion 52-4.

Beck JG; Stanley MA; Zebb BJ. Characteristics of generalized anxiety disorder in older adults: a descriptive study. *Behaviour Research and Therapy*, 1996 Mar, 34(3):225-34.

Small GW. Recognizing and treating anxiety in the elderly. *Journal of Clinical Psychiatry*, 1997, 58 Suppl 3:41-7; discussion 48-50.

Orrell M; Bebbington P. Psychosocial stress and anxiety in senile dementia. *Journal of Affective Disorders*, 1996 Jul 29, 39(3):165-73.

Lindesay J. Neurotic disorders in the elderly: often missed, poorly treated [editorial]. *British Journal of Hospital Medicine*, 1997 Apr 2-15, 57(7): 304-5.

Byrne GJ; Raphael B. The psychological symptoms of conjugal bereavement in elderly men over the first 13 months. *International Journal of Geriatric Psychiatry*, 1997 Feb, 12(2):241-51.

Prigerson HG; Shear MK; Newsom JT; Frank E; Reynolds CF 3rd; Maciejewski PK; Houck PR; Bierhals AJ; Kupfer DJ. Anxiety among widowed elders: is it distinct from depression and grief? *Anxiety*, 1996, 2(1):1-12.

Rozenzweig A; Prigerson H; Miller MD; Reynolds CF 3rd. Bereavement and late-life depression: grief and its complications in the elderly. *Annual Review of Medicine*, 1997, 48:421-8.

Smith SL; Sherrill KA; Colenda CC. Assessing and treating anxiety in elderly persons. *Psychiatric Services*, 1995 Jan, 46(1):36-42.

Casten RJ; Parmelee PA; Kleban MH; Lawton MP; Katz IR. The relationships among anxiety, depression, and pain in a geriatric institutionalized sample. *Pain*, 1995 May, 61(2):271-6.

Bleiker EM; van der Ploeg HM; Mook J; Kleijn WC. Anxiety, anger, and depression in elderly women. *Psychological Reports*, 1993 Apr, 72(2): 567-74.

Flint AJ. Epidemiology and comorbidity of anxiety disorders in the elderly. *American Journal of Psychiatry*, 1994 May, 151(5):640-9.

Hocking LB; Koenig HG. Anxiety in medically ill older patients: a review and update. *International Journal of Psychiatry in Medicine*, 1995, 25(3): 221-38.

Markovitz PJ. Treatment of anxiety in the elderly. *Journal of Clinical Psychiatry*, 1993 May, 54 Suppl:64-8.

Marriott P; Smith R. The elderly agoraphobic: a hidden problem. *Australian Family Physician*, 1993 Nov, 22(11):2036-7, 2040-1, 2044-5.

Raj BA; Corvea MH; Dagon EM. The clinical characteristics of panic disorder in the elderly: a retrospective study. *Journal of Clinical Psychiatry*, 1993 Apr, 54(4):150-5.

Simington JA; Laing GP. Effects of therapeutic touch on anxiety in the institutionalized elderly. *Clinical Nursing Research*, 1993 Nov, 2(4): 438-

50.

Tucker GJ. Introduction. Part I. Treatment approaches to anxiety, depression, and aggression in the elderly. *Journal of Clinical Psychiatry*, 1994 Feb, 55 Suppl:3-4.

10. MEDICAL PROBLEMS

Ancalzi RA; Gemma A; Marra C; Muzzolon R; Capparella O; Carbonin P. Chronic obstructive pulmonary disease. An original model of cognitive decline. *American Review of Respiratory Disease*, 1993 Aug, 148(2):418-24.

Pennypacker LC; Allen RH; Kelly JP; Matthews LM; Grigsby J; Kaye K; Lindenbaum J; Stabler SP. High prevalence of cobalamin deficiency in elderly outpatients [see comments]. *Journal of the American Geriatrics Society*, 1992 Dec, 40(12): 1197-204.

Colledge NR; Barr-Hamilton RM; Lewis SJ; Sellar RJ; Wilson JA. Evaluation of investigations to diagnose the cause of dizziness in elderly people: a community based controlled study. *BMJ* (Clinical Research Ed.), 1996 Sep 28, 313(7060): 788-92.

Sullivan M; Clark MR; Katon WJ; Fischl M; Russo J; Dobie RA; Voorhees R. Psychiatric and otologic diagnoses in patients complaining of dizziness [see comments]. *Archives of Internal Medicine*, 1993 Jun 28, 153(12):1479-84.

Grimby A; Rosenhall U. Health-related quality of life and dizziness in old age [see comments]. *Gerontology*, 1995, 41(5):286-98.

Sloane PD; Hartman M; Mitchell CM. Psychological factors associated with chronic dizziness in patients aged 60 and older. *Journal of the American Geriatrics Society*, 1994 Aug, 42(8): 847-2.

Fooken I. Sexuality in the later years--the impact of health and body-image in a sample of older women. *Patient Education and Counseling*, 1994 Jul, 23(3):227-33.

Sharma, A.; Newton, W. (1995) Clonidine as a drug of abuse. *J Am Board Fam Pract* Mar-Apr; 8(2):136-8

Bonkovsky, H.L.; Kane, R.E.; Jones, D.P.; Galinsky, R.E.; Banner, B. (1994) Acute hepatic and renal toxicity from low doses of acetaminophen in the absence of alcohol abuse or malnutrition: evidence for increased susceptibility to drug toxicity due to cardiopulmonary and renal insuf-ficiency. *Hepatology* May;19(5):1141-8

McInnes, E.; Powell, J. (1994) Drug and alcohol referrals: are elderly substance abuse diagnoses and referrals being missed? *British medical Journal* Feb 12;308 (6926):444-6

Marcus, M.T. (1993) Alcohol and other drug abuse in elders [published erratum appears in J ET Nurs 1993 Jul-Aug;20(4):168] *J ET Nurs* May-Jun;20(3):106-10

Finch, J. (1993) Prescription drug abuse. North Carolina Governor's Institute on Alcohol and Substance Abuse, Durham. *Primary Care* Mar; 20(1): 231-9

Kumar, P.D.; Chandrasekharan, K.G. (1992) 'Cauliflower ear' in an Indian patient with drug abuse [letter] *J Assoc Physicians India* Jul;40(7): 491.

Solomon. K.; Manepalli, J.; Ireland,G.A.; Mahon, G.M. (1993) Alcoholism and prescription drug abuse in the elderly: St. Louis University grand rounds [clinical conference] *Journal of the American Geriatrics Society* 41(1):57-69

Rice, D.P.; Kelman, S.; Miller, L.S. (1991) Economic costs of drug abuse. *NIDA Research Mono-*

graphs;113:10-32

Hauser, A.C.; Derfler, K.; Balcke, P. (1991) Progression of renal insufficiency in analgesic nephropathy: impact of continuous drug abuse. *J Clin Epidemiol*;44(1):53-6

Jinks, M.J.; Raschko, R.R. (1990) A profile of alcohol and prescription drug abuse in a high-risk community-based elderly population. *DICP* 24(10): 971-5

Chenitz, W.C.; Salisbury, S.; Stone, J.T. (1990) Drug misuse and abuse in the elderly. *Issues Ment Health Nurs* 11(1):1-16

Rice, D.P.; Kelman, S. (1989) Measuring comorbidity and overlap in the hospitalization cost for alcohol and drug abuse and mental illness. *Inquiry* Summer;26(2):249-60

el-Mallakh, R.S. (1989) Migraine headaches and drug abuse [letter] *South Med J* 82(6):805

Giannini, A.J. (1988) Drug abuse and depression: possible models for geriatric anorexia. *Neurobiol Aging* Jan-Feb;9(1):26-7

Cosgrove, R.(1988) Understanding drug abuse in the elderly. *Midwife Health Visit Community Nurse* Jun;24(6):222-3

Weiss, K.J.; Greenfield, D.P. (1986) Prescription drug abuse. *Psychiatr Clin North Am* Sep;9(3): 475-90

Wade, M. (1987) Meeting the challenge of alcohol and drug abuse in the older adult. *Home Healthc Nurse* Sep-Oct;5(5):19, 22-3

Shelowitz, P.A. (1987) Drug use, misuse, and abuse among the elderly. *Med Law* ;6(3):235-50

Granella, F.; Farina, S.; Malferrari, G.; Manzoni, G.C. (1987) Drug abuse in chronic headache: a clinico-epidemiologic study. *Cephalalgia* Mar;7(1):15-9

Caroselli-Karinja, M. (1985) Drug abuse and the elderly. *J Psychosoc Nurs Ment Health Serv* Jun;23(6):25-30

Hasin, D.; Endicott, J, (1985) Alcohol and drug abuse in patients with affective syn-dromes. *Compr Psychiatry* May-Jun; 26(3): 283- 95

11. PAIN

Dodrill, C.B. (1997) Myths of neuropsychology. *The Clinical Neuropsychologist.* 11, 1-17.

Eccleston, C. (1994) Chronic pain and attention: A cognitive approach. *British Journal of Clinical Psychology* 33: 535-47.

Eccleston, C. (1995) Chronic pain and distraction: An experimental investigation into the role of sustained and shifting attention in the processing of chronic persistent pain. *Behavior Research & Therapy.* 33(4): 391-405.

Grigsby, J., Rosenburg, N.L. & Busenbark, D. (1995) Chronic pain is associated with deficits in information processing. *Perceptual and Motor Skills.* 81,403-410.

Schwartz, D.P., Earth, J.T., Dane, J.R., Drenan, S.E., DeGood, D.E. & Rowlingson, J.C. (1987) Cognitive deficits in chronic pain patients with and without a history of head/neck injury: Development of a brief screening battery. *The Clinical Journal of Pain.* 3, 94-101.

Kewman, D.G., Valshampayan, N., Zeid, D. 8 Han, B. (1991) Cognitive impairment in musculo-keletal pain patients. *International Journal of Psychiatry in Medicine.* 21(3): 253-62.

12. HEARING PROBLEMS

Andersson G; Melin L; Scott B; Lindberg P. An evaluation of a behavioural treatment approach to hearing impairment. *Behaviour Research and Therapy*, 1995 Mar, 33(3):283-92.

Andersson G; Melin L; Scott B; Lindberg P. A two-year follow-up examination of a behavioural treatment approach to hearing tactics. *British Journal of Audiology*, 1995 Dec, 29(6):347-54.

Andersson G; Green M. Anxiety in elderly hearing impaired persons. *Perceptual and Motor Skills,* 1995 Oct, 81(2):552-4.

13. VISION PROBLEMS

Pankow L; Luchins D. An optical intervention for visual hallucinations associated with visual impairment in an elderly patient. *Optometry and Vision Science,* 1997 Mar, 74(3):138-43.

Lightman JM; Rosenbloom AA. Geriatric optometry questionnaire. *Journal of the American Optometric Association*, 1991 Jun, 62(6):472-4.

Bab, Werner. *The uses of psychology in geriatric ophthalmology.* Springfield, Ill., Thomas [1964].

14. HALLUCINATIONS

Anderson SW, Rizzo M. Hallucinations following occipital lobe damage: the pathological activation of visual representations. *Journal of Clinical and Experimental Neuropsychology.* 1994;16(5): 651-663.

Arnow, A. J. Verbal hallucinations: a restitutional symptom. *Bull. Menninger Clin.*, 1952, 16: 178-183.

Dewi-Rees, W. (1971) The hallucinations of widowhood. *British Medical Journal.* 3:3741.

Auditory hallucinations and subvocal speech; objective study in a case of schizophrenia. *Journal of Nervous and Mental Disease,* (1949) 109:418-427.

Berries GE, Brook P. The Charles Bonnet syndrome and the problem of visual perceptual disorders in the elderly. *Age Aging.* 1982:2: 17-23.

Chen J; Gomez M; Veit S; O' Dowd MA. Visual hallucinations in a blind elderly woman: Charles Bonnet syndrome, an under-recognized clinical condition [letter]. *General Hospital Psychiatry*, 1996 Nov, 18(6):453-5.

Eisendrath SJ, Sweeney MA. Toxic neuropsychiatric effects of digoxin at therapeutic serum concentrations. *American Journal of Psychiatry.* 1987; 144(4): 506 -507.

Erickson, GD & Gustafson, GJ. Controlling auditory hallucination. *Hospital and Community Psychiatry*, 1968, 19: 327-329.

Fornazzari I, Farcnik K, Smith I, et al. Violent visual hallucinations and aggression in frontal lobe dysfunction: clinical manifestations of deep orbito-frontal foci. *Journal of Neuropsychiatry and Clinical Neuroscience.* 1992;4(1):42-44,

Goffey CE, Cummings, JL, eds. *American Psychiatric Press Textbook of Geriatric Neuropsychiatry.* Washington: American Psy-chiatric Press; 1994.

Grossberg GT; Manepalli J. The older patient with psychotic symptoms. *Psychiatric Serv-ices*, 1995 Jan, 46(1):55-9.

Holroyd S, Rabins PV, Finkelstein D, et al. Visual hallucinations in patients with macular degeneration. *American Journal of Psychiatry*, 1992; 149 (12): 1701-1 706.

Lalla D; Primeau F. Complex visual hallucinations in macular degeneration. Canadian Journal of Psychiatry. Revue *Canadienne de Psychiatrie*, 1993 Nov, 38(9):584-6.

Maricle RA, Turner LD, Lehman KD. The Charles Bonnet syndrome: a brief review and case report. *Psychiatric Services*. 1995;46(4): 289 -291.

Snavely SR, Hedges GR. The neurotoxicity of antibacterial agents. *Annals of Internal Medicine*. 1984; 101(1):92-104.

Stewart JT, Yelton JA. Treatment of organic hallucinosis with carbamazepine. *Am J Psychiatry*. 1945;152(1):150. Letter.

Teunisse RJ; Cruysberg JR; Hoefnagels WH; Verbeek AL; Zitman FG. Visual hallucinations in psychologically normal people: Charles Bonnet's syndrome. *Lancet*, 1996 Mar 23, 347(9004): 794-7.

Teunisse RJ; Cruysberg JR; Verbeek A; Zitman FG.The Charles Bonnet syndrome: a large prospective study in The Netherlands. A study of the prevalence of the Charles Bonnet syndrome and associated factors in 500 patients attending the University Department of Ophthalmology at Nijmegen [see comments]. *British Journal of Psychiatry,* 1995 Feb, 166(2):254-7.

(1950) Verbal hallucinations as automatic speech: The reactivation of dormant speech habit. *American Journal of Psychiatry*. 107:110.

15. DELUSIONS

Karkalas, Y. & Nicotra, M. (1969) The capgras syndrome: a rare psychiatric condition. Love -hate conflict resolved by directing ambivalent feelings to an imagined double. *R I Med J* Aug;52(8): 452-4

Arthur, A. Z. (1964) Theories and explanations of delusions: a review. *American Journal of Psychiatry*, 121: 105-115.

Swanson, DW, Bohert, PJ. and Smith, JA (1970) *The Paranoid*. Boston: Little, Brown & Co.

Di Bella, GAW. (1977) Educating Staff to Manage Threatening Paranoid Patients. *American Journal of Psychiatry*, 136:3, March, 333-335.

Meissner, WW. (1986) *Psychotherapy and the Paranoid Process*, Northvale, New Jersey, London: Jason Aronson Inc.

Newhill, C.E. (1990) The Role of Culture in the Development of Paranoid Symptomatology." *American Journal of Orthopsychiatry*, 60(2): 176-185.

Roth, M. (1989) Delusional (Paranoid) Dis-orders. In Treatments of Psychiatric Disorders, A Task Force Report of the American Psychiatric Association, Vol. 2. Washington: American Psychiatric Association.

Sparr, LF, Boehnlein, JK and Cooney, TG (1986) The Medical Management of the Paranoid Patient. *General Hospital Psychiatry*, 8:49-55.

Walker, JI. and Cavenar, Jr. JO. (1983) Paranoid Symptoms and Conditions. In *Signs and Symptoms in Psychiatry,* edited by JO. Cavenar, Jr. & HK. Brodie. Philadelphia: J.B. Lippincott.

16. STROKES

Rusin MJ. (1990) Stroke rehabilitation: a geropsych-ological perspective. *Archives of Physical Med-icine and Rehabilitation*, Oct, 71(11): 914 -22.

Senelick R. & Rossi, P. (1994) *Living With Stroke* Contemporary Books, Chicago,

Donahue, PJ *How to Prevent Stroke* Rodale Press,

Emmaus, Pennsylvania, 1989

17. BEHAVIOR PROBLEMS

Maletta, G. (1992) Behavioral problems that are not amenable to drug therapy *Int. Psychogeriatr.* 4(supplement I):117-130.

Taft, L.B.; Barkin, R.L. (1990) Drug abuse? Use and misuse of psychotropic drugs in Alzheimer's care. *J Gerontol Nurs* 16(8):4-10.

Dawson, PG & Wells, DL (1992) A Content Methodology for Advancing Gerontological Nursing Practice. *Clinical Nurse Specialist* 6(2):85-88.

Busse, Ewald W. and Blazer, Dan G.(1996) *The Amer-ican psychiatric press textbook of geriatric psychiatry* / edited by   2nd ed. Washington, DC : American Psychiatric Press,.

Dyck G. (1997) Management of geriatric behavior prob-lems. *Psychiatric Clinics of North America*, Mar, 20(1):165-80.

Lawton MP. Behavioral problems and interventions in Alzheimer's disease: research needs. *International Psychogeriatrics*, 1996, 8 Suppl 1:95-8.

Drench ME; Losee RH. Sexuality and sexual capacities of elderly people. *Rehabilitation Nursing,* 1996 May-Jun, 21(3):118-23.

18. ASSESSMENTS

Reisberg B, Ferris SH: (1982) Diagnosis and assessment of the older patient. *Hospital and Community Psychiatry* 33:104-110,

Brain, R. W. (1955) Agnosia, apraxia and aphasia, Chapter 83, Vol. 3. In S. AK. Wilson and AN Bruce (eds.), Neurology. Baltimore: Williams and Wilkins Co.

Anderson, GP (1992) How to assess the older mind *RN* July 34-39.

Folslein. M., & Folslein;. S (1990). Mental status examination. in the Merck manual geriatrics. Merck .

Abraham, Ivo (1992) Geriatric Mental Health: Assessing Geriatric Patients *Journal of Psychosocial Nursing* 30(9):13-19.

Anderson, Gayle (1992) How to assess the older mind *RN* 34-40

Burns, S; Kappenberg R; McKenna A; Wood C (1994) Brain injury: personality, psychopath-logy and neuropsychology. *Brain Injury* Jul;8(5): 413-27

Damasio, A.R. (1992) Neuropsychology, dementia and aging. *Current Opinions in Neurology and Neurosurgery* Feb;5(1):145-71.

Bell IR; Amend D; Kaszniak AW; Schwartz GE; Peterson JM; Stini WA; Miller JW; Selhub J.Trait shyness in the elderly: evidence for an association with Parkinson's disease in family members and biochemical correlates. *Journal of Geriatric Psychiatry and Neurology,* 1995 Jan, 8(1):16-22.

Fidler, G.S. (1984) *Design of rehabilitation services in psychiatric hospital settings.* RAMSCO Publishing, Laurel, MD.

Gurland, B.; Golden, R.; Teresi J. Challop, J. (1984) The SHORT-CARE: An efficient instrument for the assessment of depression, dementia, and disability. *Journal of Gerontology* 39(2):166-169.

Koss, E. (1994) Neuropsychology and Alzheimer's disease. *Clin. Geriatric Medicine* 10(2):299-313.

19. INTERVENTIONS

Whitbourne SK; Culgin S; Cassidy E. (1995) Evaluation of infantilizing intonation and content of speech directed at the aged. *International Journal of Aging and Human Development,*, 41(2): 109-16.

Ryan EB; Hamilton JM; See SK. Patronizing the old: how do younger and older adults respond to baby talk in the nursing home? *International Journal of Aging and Human Development*, 1994, 39(1):21-32.

Thomas LH.A comparison of the verbal interactions of qualified nurses and nursing auxiliaries in primary, team and functional nursing wards. *International Journal of Nursing Studies*, 1994 Jun, 31(3):231-44.

Orange JB; Lubinski RB; Higginbotham DJ. Conversational repair by individuals with dementia of the Alzheimer's type. *Journal of Speech and Hearing Research,* 1996 Aug, 39(4):881-95.

20. MANAGING SPECIFIC BEHAVIOR PROBLEMS

CATASTROPHIC REACTION

Starkstein SE; Fedoroff JP; Price TR; Leiguarda R; Robinson RG. Catastrophic reaction after cerebrovascular lesions: frequency, correlates, and validation of a scale. *Journal of Neuropsychiatry and Clinical Neurosciences,* 1993 Spring, 5(2): 189-94.

Teasell R. Catastrophic reaction after stroke. A case study. *American Journal of Physical Medicine and Rehabilitation*, 1993 Jun, 72(3): 151-3.

EATING PROBLEMS

Sidenvall B; Fjellstrom C; Ek AC. Cultural perspectives of meals expressed by patients in geriatric care. *International Journal of Nursing Studies*, 1996 Apr, 33(2):212-22.

De Castro JM. Age-related changes in spontaneous food intake and hunger in humans. *Appetite*, 1993 Dec, 21(3):255-72.

Lange-Alberts ME; Shott S. Nutritional intake. Use of touch and verbal cuing. *Journal of Gerontological Nursing,* 1994 Feb, 20(2):36-40.

Ackerman BH; Kasbekar N. Disturbances of taste and smell induced by drugs. *Pharmacotherapy,* 1997 May-Jun, 17(3):482-96.

Duffy VB; Backstrand JR; Ferris AM. Olfactory dysfunction and related nutritional risk in free-living, elderly women. *Journal of the American Dietetic Association*, 1995 Aug, 95(8): 879-84; quiz 885-6.

De Jong N; De Graaf C; Van Staveren WA. Effect of sucrose in breakfast items on pleasantness and food intake in the elderly. *Physiology and Behavior*, 1996 Dec, 60(6): 1453-62.

Steele CM; Greenwood C; Ens I; Robertson C; Seidman-Carlson R. Mealtime difficulties in a home for the aged: not just dysphagia. *Dysphagia,* 1997 Winter, 12(1):43-50; discussion 51.

Schiffman SS; Warwick ZS. Effect of flavor enhancement of foods for the elderly on nutritional status: food intake, biochemical indices, and anthropometric measures. *Physiology and Behavior*, 1993 Feb, 53(2):395-402.

Watson R. Measuring feeding difficulty in patients with dementia: perspectives and problems. *Jour-nal of Advanced Nursing*, 1993 Jan, 18(1):25-31.

Rolls BJ. Appetite, hunger, and satiety in the elderly. *Critical Reviews in Food Science and Nutrition,* 1993, 33(1):39-44.

Bonnel WB. The nursing home group dining room: managing the work of eating. *Journal of Nutrition for the Elderly,* 1993, 13(1):1-10.

Chidester JC; Spangler AA. Fluid intake in the institutionalized elderly. *Journal of the American Dietetic Association,* 1997 Jan, 97(1):23-8; quiz 29-30.

Watson R. The Mokken scaling procedure (MSP) applied to the measurement of feeding difficulty in elderly people with dementia. *International Jour-nal of Nursing Studies,* 1996 Aug, 33(4): 385-93.

Ortega RM; Manas LR; Andres P; Gaspar MJ; Agudo FR; Jimenez A; Pascual T. Functional and psychic deterioration in elderly people may be aggravated by folate deficiency. *Journal of Nutrition,* 1996 Aug, 126(8):1992-9.

Zawada ET Jr. Malnutrition in the elderly. Is it simply a matter of not eating enough? *Post-graduate Medicine,* 1996 Jul, 100(1):207-8, 211-4, 220-2 passim.

Gloth FM 3rd; Tobin JD; Smith CE; Meyer JN. Nutrient intakes in a frail homebound elderly population in the community vs a nursing home population. *Journal of the American Dietetic Association,* 1996 Jun, 96(6):605-7.

Birchall R; Waters KR. What do elderly people do in hospital? *Journal of Clinical Nursing,* 1996 May, 5(3):171-6.

Holzapfel SK; Ramirez RF; Layton MS; Smith IW; Sagl-Massey K; DuBose JZ. Feeder position and food and fluid consumed by nursing home residents. *Journal of Gerontological Nursing,* 1996 Apr, 22(4):6-12.

Rolls BJ; Dimeo KA; Shide DJ. Age-related impairments in the regulation of food intake. *American Journal of Clinical Nutrition,* 1995 Nov, 62(5):923-31.

Sone Y. Age-associated problems in nutrition. *Applied Human Science,* 1995 Sep, 14(5):201-10.

Aronow WS. Post-prandial hypotension in the elderly. *Journal of the Royal Society of Medicine,* 1995 Sep, 88(9):499-501.

Aronow WS; Ahn C. Postprandial hypotension in 499 elderly persons in a long-term health care facility [see comments]. *Journal of the American Geriatrics Society,* 1994 Sep, 42(9):930-2.

Farnsworth TA; Heseltine D. The effect of postprandial hypotension on rehabilitation of the frail elderly with cerebrovascular disease. *Journal of International Medical Research,* 1994 Mar- Apr, 22(2):77-84.

Frisoni GB; Franzoni S; Rozzini R; Ferrucci L; Boffelli S; Trabucchi M. Food intake and mortality in the frail elderly. *Journals of Gerontology. Series A, Biological Sciences and Medical Sciences,* 1995 Jul, 50(4):M203-10.

De Castro JM. Age-related changes in spontaneous food intake and hunger in humans. *Appetite,* 1993 Dec, 21(3):255-72.

Hall P; Driscoll R. Anorexia in the elderly--an annotation. *International Journal of Eating Disorders,* 1993 Dec, 14(4):497-9.

Keller HH. Malnutrition in institutionalized elderly: how and why? *Journal of the American Geriatrics Society,* 1993 Nov, 41(11):1212-8.

Stock LZ; Milan MA. Improving dietary practices of elderly individuals: the power of prompting feedback, and social reinforcement. *Journal of Applied Behavior Analysis,* 1993 Fall, 26(3): 379-87.

Lipski PS; Torrance A; Kelly PJ; James OF. A

study of nutritional deficits of long-stay geriatric patients [see comments]. *Age and Ageing,* 1993 Jul, 22(4):244-55.

Rosenbloom CA; Whittington FJ. The effects of bereavement on eating behaviors and nutrient intakes in elderly widowed persons. *Journal of Gerontology,* 1993 Jul, 48(4):S223-9.

Dwyer J. A vital sign: progress and prospects in nutrition screening of older Americans. *Aging,* 1993 Apr, 5(2 Suppl 1):13-21.

Boukaiba N; Flament C; Acher S; Chappuis P; Piau A; Fusselier M; Dardenne M; Lemonnier D. A physiological amount of zinc supplemen-tation: effects on nutritional, lipid, and thymic status in an elderly population. *American Journal of Clinical Nutrition,* 1993 Apr, 57(4):566-72.

Tan CD; Hart LL. Caffeine in elderly patients with postprandial hypotension. *Annals of Pharma cotherapy,* 1993 Jun, 27(6):732-3.

Jansen RW; Connelly CM; Kelley-Gagnon MM; Parker JA; Lipsitz LA. Postprandial hypotension in elderly patients with unexplained syncope. *Archives of Internal Medicine,* 1995 May 8, 155 (9): 945-52.

Casper RC. Nutrition and its relationship to aging. *Experimental Gerontology,* 1995 May-Aug, 30 (3-4):299-314.

Lewis CW; Frongillo EA Jr; Roe DA. Drug -nutrient interactions in three long-term-care facilities. *Journal of the American Dietetic Association,* 1995 Mar, 95(3):309-15.

Jansson L; Norberg A; Sandman PO; Astrom G. When the severely ill elderly patient refuses food. Ethical reasoning among nurses. *Inter-national Journal of Nursing Studies,* 1995 Feb, 32(1): 68-78.

Nikolaus T; Bach M; Siezen S; Volkert D; Oster P; Schlierf G. Assessment of nutritional risk in the elderly. *Annals of Nutrition and Metabolism,* 1995, 39(6):340-5.

McCargar LJ; Hotson BL; Nozza A. Fibre and nutrient intakes of chronic care elderly patients. *Journal of Nutrition for the Elderly,* 1995, 15(1):13-30.

Stitt S; O'Connell C; Grant D. Old, poor & malnourished. *Nutrition and Health,* 1995, 10(2): 135-54.

Sidenvall B; Fjellstrom C; Ek AC. The meal situation in geriatric care--intentions and experiences. *Journal of Advanced Nursing,* 1994 Oct, 20(4):613-21.

Hetherington MM; Burnett L. Ageing and the pursuit of slimness: dietary restraint and weight satisfaction in elderly women. *British Journal of Clinical Psychology,* 1994 Sep, 33 (Pt 3):391-400.

Watson R; Deary IJ. Measuring feeding difficulty in patients with dementia: multivariate analysis of feeding problems, nursing intervention and indicators of feeding difficulty. *Journal of Advanced Nursing,* 1994 Aug, 20(2):283-7.
Rolls BJ. Appetite and satiety in the elderly. *Nutrition Reviews,* 1994 Aug, 52(8 Pt 2):S9-10.

SLEEP PROBLEMS

Feinsilver SH; Hertz G. Sleep in the elderly patient. *Clinics in Chest Medicine,* 1993 Sep, 14(3):405-11.

Sloan EP; Flint AJ; Reinish L; Shapiro CM. Circadian rhythms and psychiatric disorders in the elderly. *Journal of Geriatric Psychiatry and Neurology,* 1996 Oct, 9(4):164-70.

Miles LE. Dement WC: Sleep and aging *Sleep* 3:119-220, 1980

Resestein QR: Insomnia and sleep disrurbances in the aged: sleep and insomnia in the elderly. *Journal of Geriatric Psychiatry* 13:153-171, 1980.

Bixler EO, Kales A, Soldaros CR, et al: Prevalence of sleep disorders in the Los Angeles metropolitan area. *American Journal of Psychiatry* 136:1257 -1262. 1979.

Institute of Medicine: *Sleeping pills, insomnia, and medical practice*. Washington, DC, National Academy of Sciences, 1979 7.

Kales A, Bixler EO, Tan TL, et al (1974) Chronic hypnotic-drug use: ineffectiveness, drug withdrawal insomnia, and dependence. *JAMA* 227:513-517.

Roffwarg HP, Muzio NJ, Dement WC (1966) Ontogenetic development of the human sleep cycle. Science 152: 619.

Feinberg I, Koresko RL, Heller N: EEG sleep patterns as a function of normal and pathological aging in man. *Journal of Psychiatric Research* 5:107- 144, 1967
Williams RL, Karacan I. Hursch CJ: flee rroe ncep halograp h y (EEG) of Human Sleep: Clinical Applications. New York, Wiley, 1974

Webb W (1974) The rhythms of sleep and waking, in *Chronobiology* Sheving L, Halberg F, Pauly. EDS. Tokyo, Jgaku Shoin

Ancoli-Israel S, Kripke D., Mason W (1981) Sleep apnea and nocturnal myoclonus in a senile population. *Sleep* 4:349- 358.

Reynolds C., Spiker D., Hanin I, et al: (1983) EEG sleep, aging, and psychopathology. new data and stare of the art. *Biological Psychiatry* 18:133-155.

Roffwarg HP: (1982) Diagnostic classification of sleep and arousal disorders. *Sleep* 2:1, 1379 15. *Association of Sleep Disorders Centers*, US Public Health Service, and Upjohn Co: project Sleep Educational Program. Kalamazoo, MI, Upjohn.

Webb W, Swinburne H (1971) An observational study of sleep in the aged. *Perceptual Motor Skills* 32:895-838, 1971.

Winger C, Vernikos-Daneilis J, Cronin S, et al (1972) Circadian rhythm asynchrony in man during hypokinesis. *Journal of Applied Physiology* 33: 640-643.

RESISTING CARE

Nelson F. The development of an indirect self-destructive behavior scaled for use with chronically ill medical patients. *International Journal of Social Psychiatry* 28(1):5-13

Potts HW; Richie MF; Kaas MJ. Resistance to care. *Journal of Gerontological Nursing*, 1996 Nov, 22(11):11-6.

Carlson DL; Fleming KC; Smith GE; Evans JM. Management of dementia-related behavioral disturbances: a nonpharmacologic approach. *Mayo Clinic Proceedings*, 1995 Nov, 70(11):1108-15.

YELLING

Morse JM; Intrieri RC. 'Talk to me' patient communication in a long-term care facility. *Journal of Psychosocial Nursing and Mental Health Services*, 1997 May, 35(5):34-9.

Bentham PW; Jones S; Hodges JR. A comparison of semantic memory in vascular dementia and dementia of Alzheimer's type. *International Journal of Geriatric Psychiatry*, 1997 May, 12(5):575-80.

Gibbons P; Gannon M; Wrigley M. A study of

aggression among referrals to a community-based psychiatry of old age service. *International Journal of Geriatric Psychiatry*, 1997 Mar, 12(3):384-8.

Farrell Miller M. Physical aggressive resident behavior during hygienic care. *Journal of Gerontological Nursing*, 1997 May, 23(5):24-39.

Shapiro, Deane H.; Sandman, Curt A.; Grossman, Michael; Grossman, Barbara. Aging and sense of control. *Psychological Reports,* 1995 Oct, v77 (n2):616-618.

DANGEROUS MOVES

Camicioli R; Howieson D; Lehman S; Kaye J. Talking while walking: the effect of a dual task in aging and Alzheimer's disease. *Neurology*, 1997 Apr, 48(4):955-8.

Miller PA. Suggestions for improving a falls prevention program [letter; comment]. *Gerontologist*, 1992 Dec, 32(6):859.

Stewart RB; Moore MT; May FE; Marks RG; Hale WE. Nocturia: a risk factor for falls in the elderly. *Journal of the American Geriatrics Society*, 1992 Dec, 40(12):1217-20.

Suzuki M; Okamura T; Shimazu Y; Takahashi H; Eguchi K; Kano K; Tsuchiya S. [A study of falls experienced by institutionalized elderly]. Nippon Koshu Eisei Zasshi *Japanese Journal of Public Health,* 1992 Dec, 39(12):927-40.

Ginter SF; Mion LC. Falls in the nursing home: preventable or inevitable? *Journal of Gerontological Nursing*, 1992 Nov, 18(11):43-8.

Petit CD. Falls in the elderly. *Journal - South Carolina Medical Association*, 1992 Nov, 88(11): 541-5.

Croft W; Foraker S. Working together to prevent falls. *Rn,* 1992 Nov, 55(11):17-8, 20.

Richardson JK; Ching C; Hurvitz EA. The relationship between electromyographically documented peripheral neuropathy and falls. *Journal of the American Geriatrics Society*, 1992 Oct, 40 (10):1008-12.

Sorock GS; Labiner DM. Peripheral neuromuscular dysfunction and falls in an elderly cohort. *American Journal of Epidemiology*, 1992 Sep 1, 136(5):584-91.

Shipman KH. Do restraints prevent falls? [letter; comment]. *Annals of Internal Medicine,* 1992 Sep 1, 117(5):442-3.

Using muscle in the fight against falls [news]. *American Journal of Nursing*, 1992 Sep, 92(9):12.

Corbett C; Pennypacker B. Using a quality improvement team to reduce patient falls. *Journal for Healthcare Quality,* 1992 Sep-Oct, 14(5): 38-41, 44-54.

Reinsch S; MacRae P; Lachenbruch PA; Tobis JS. Attempts to prevent falls and injury: a prospective community study [see comments]. Gerontologist, 1992 Aug, 32(4):450-6.

Weller C; Humphrey SJ; Kirollos C; Bowes SG; Charlett A; Dobbs SM; Dobbs RJ. Gait on a shoestring: falls and foot separation in parkinsonism. *Age and Ageing*, 1992 Jul, 21(4):242-4.

Cwikel J; Fried AV. The social epidemiology of falls among community-dwelling elderly: guidelines for prevention. *Disability and Rehabilitation*, 1992 Jul-Sep, 14(3):113-21.

Cwikel J. Falls among elderly people living at home: medical and social factors in a national sample [see comments]. *Israel Journal of Medical Sciences*, 1992 Jul, 28(7):446-53.

Sumner ED; Simpson WM Jr. Intervention in falls among the elderly. *Journal of Practical Nursing*, 1992 Jun, 42(2):24-34.

Perlin E. Preventing falls in the elderly. A practical approach to a common problem. *Postgraduate Medicine*, 1992 Jun, 91(8):237-8, 241, 244.

Hale WA; Delaney MJ; McGaghie WC. Characteristics and predictors of falls in elderly patients. *Journal of Family Practice*, 1992 May, 34(5):577-81.

Lawrence JI; Maher PL. An interdisciplinary falls consult team: a collaborative approach to patient falls. *Journal of Nursing Care Quality*, 1992 Apr, 6(3):21-9.

Spellbring AM. Assessing elderly patients at high risk for falls: a reliability study. *Journal of Nursing Care Quality*, 1992 Apr, 6(3):30-5.

Vellas B; Baumgartner RN; Wayne SJ; Conceicao J; Lafont C; Albarede JL; Garry PJ. Relationship between malnutrition and falls in the elderly. *Nutrition*, 1992 Mar-Apr, 8(2):105-8.

Blake AJ. Falls in the elderly. *British Journal of Hospital Medicine*, 1992 Feb 19-Mar 3, 47(4): 268 -72.

Jech AO. Preventing falls in the elderly. *Geriatric Nursing*, 1992 Jan-Feb, 13(1):43-4.

Lord SR; Clark RD; Webster IW. Physiological factors associated with falls in an elderly population. *Journal of the American Geriatrics Society*, 1991 Dec, 39(12):1194-200.

Cumming RG; Miller JP; Kelsey JL; Davis P; Arfken CL; Birge SJ; Peck WA. Medications and multiple falls in elderly people: the St Louis OASIS study. *Age and Ageing*, 1991 Nov, 20(6): 455-61.

Sherman D. Medication use and falls. *Contemporary Longterm Care*, 1991 Nov, 14(11): 66, 68.

Fleming BE; Wilson DR; Pendergast DR. A portable, easily performed muscle power test and its association with falls by elderly persons [see comments]. *Archives of Physical Medicine and Rehabilitation*, 1991 Oct, 72(11):886-

White D. Old age is not a reason to fall. *Nursing Standard*, 1991 Nov 13-19, 6(8):20-1.

Ross JE. Iatrogenesis in the elderly. Contributors to falls. *Journal of Gerontological Nursing*, 1991 Sep, 17(9):19-23.

Fried AV; Cwikel J; Ring H; Galinsky D. ELGAM--extra-laboratory gait assessment method: identification of risk factors for falls among the elderly at home. *International Disability Studies*, 1990 Oct-Dec, 12(4):161-4.

Hale WA; Delaney MJ; McGaghie WC. Predicting elderly patients' mobility using fall history and physician assessment. *Family Medicine*, 1990 Sep- Oct, 22(5):383-7.

Nelson RC; Amin MA. Falls in the elderly. *Emergency Medicine Clinics of North America*, 1990 May, 8(2):309-24.

Wright BA; Aizenstein S; Vogler G; Rowe M; Miller C. Frequent fallers—Leading groups to identify psychological factors. *Journal of Gerontological Nursing*, 1990 Apr, 16(4):15-9.

Vlahov D; Myers AH; al-Ibrahim MS. Epidemiology of falls among patients in a rehabilitation hospital. *Archives of Physical Medicine and Rehabilitation*, 1990 Jan, 71(1):8-12.

Wells. Y. Jorm. A. (1987) Evaluation of a special nursing home unit for dementia sufferers: A randomized controlled comparison with community care. *Aust N Z Journ Psychiatry* 21:524-

531.

Beland, I. (1980) Burn-out Syndrome in Nurses, in Werner-Beland *Grief Processes in Long Term Illness* Reston Publishers, Reston VA.

Astrom S; Nilsson M; Norberg A; Sandman PO; Winblad B. Staff burnout in dementia care-relations to empathy and attitudes. *International Journal of Nursing Studies*, 1991, 28(1): 65-75.

Joshua R. Shua-Haim, MD Joel S. Gross, MD Stratford, NJ Lesch-Nyan Syndrome in an Alzheimer's Patient *Nursing Home Medicine* June 1997 Vol. 5, No. 7

Loebel JP, Leibovici A. Management of patients with Alzheimer's and related dementias. *Med Clin North Am* 1994;4:841-859.

Kelly WN, Palella TDL. Gout and other disorders of purine metabolism. In: Harrison's *Principles of Internal Medicine*. 199133841.

AGITATION

Almeida OP; Howard RJ; Levy R; David AS; Morris RG; Sahakian BJ.Clinical and cognitive diversity of psychotic states arising in late life (late paraphrenia).*Psychological Medicine*, 1995 Jul, 25(4):699-714.

Chou KR; Kaas MJ; Richie MF. (1996) Assaultive behavior in geriatric patients. *Journal of Gerontological Nursing*, Nov, 22(11):30-8.

Cohen-Mansfield J. (1995) Assessment of disruptive be-havior/agitation in the elderly: function, methods, and difficulties. *Journal of Geriatric Psychiatry and Neurology*, Jan, 8(1):52-60.

Cohen-Mansfield J; Werner P; Watson V; Pasis S. (1995) Agitation among elderly persons at adult day-care centers: the experiences of relatives and

staff members. *International Psychogeriatrics*, Fall, 7(3):447-58.

Cohen-Mansfield J; Werner P; Watson V; Pasis S. Agitation among elderly persons at adult day-care centers: the experiences of relatives and staff members. *International Psychogeriatrics,* 1995 Fall, 7(3):447-58.

Mintzer JE; Brawman-Mintzer O. Agitation as a possible expression of generalized anxiety disorder in demented elderly patients: toward a treatment approach. *Journal of Clinical Psychiatry,* 1996, 57 Suppl 7:55-63; discussion 73-5.

Monfort JC. [Aggressivity in the elderly: when and how to treat?]. *Revue du Praticien*, 1994 Jun 1, 44(11):1426-30.

21. ASSAULT

Bender, KJ (1998) Addressing Agitation and Aggression in Dementia *Psychiatric Times*, July.

Chou, KR, et al (1996) Assaultive Behaviors in Geriatric Patients *Journal of Gerontological Nursing* November. 22(11):30-8.

Colenda, C.C., & Hamer, R.M. (1991). Antecedents and interventions for aggressive behavior of patients at a geropsychiatric state hospital. *Hospital & Community Psychiatry*, 42(3), 287-292.

Dubin W.R. (1981). Evaluating and managing the violent patient. *Annals of Emergency Medicine*, 10(9), 481-484.

Jones, M.. (1985). Patient violence. Report of 200 incidents, *Journal of Psychosocial Research Nursing and Health*, 14, 87-95. [I don't have this]

Junginger J. Psychosis and violence: the case for a content analysis of psychotic experience. *Schizophrenia Bulletin*, 1996, 22(1):91-103.

Levy, P., Hartocollis, P. Nursing aids and patient violence. *Am J Psych* 1976; 133:429-431.

Lion, J.R., Snyder, W., Merrill, G.L.: Underreporting of assaults in staff in state hospitals. *Hospital & Community Psychiatry* 1981; 32:497-498.

Lion JR et al (1976) A Violence clinic: Three years of Experience *American Journal of Psychiatry*; 133(4):432-435.

Maxfield, CM, et al (1996) Training Staff to Prevent Aggressive Behavior. *Journal of Gerontological Nursing* January.

Miller BL; Darby A; Benson DF; Cummings JL; Miller MH. Aggressive, socially disruptive and antisocial behaviour associated with fronto-temporal dementia. *British Journal of Psychiatry*, 1997 Feb, 170:150-4.

Rvan, J.A., & P'osner, E.C. (1989). The assaulted nurse: Short-term and long-term responses. *Archives of Psychiatric Nursing*, 3(6), 323-331.

Stokman, C.L.J.: Violence among hospitalized patients. *Hospital & Community Psychiatry* 1982; 33:986.

Whittington R; Wykes T. Aversive stimulation by staff and violence by psychiatric patients. *British Journal of Clinical Psychology*, 1996 Feb, 35 (Pt 1):11-20.

Atkinson, J.H. (1982). Managing the violent patient in the general hospital. *Post Graduate Medicine*: 71(1), 193-201. 0

Ball, G.G. (1993). Modifying the behavior of the violent patient. *Psychiatric Quarterly* 64(4), 359-369.

Barber, I.W., Hundley, P., et al (1988). Clinical and demographic characteristics oi 15 patients

with repetitively assaultive behavior. *Psychiatric Quarterly*, 59(3),213-224.

Blair, D.T., & New, S.A. (1991). Assaultive behavior: Know the risk. *Journal of Psychosocial Nursing*, 29(11), 25-29.

Blumenreich, P.E. (1993)Pharmacotherapy of violence. In PE Blumenreich, & S. Lewis (Eds.), *Managing The violent Patient: A Clinician's Guide* (pp· 53-77).New York, NY: Brunner Mazel.

Bridges-Parlet, S., Knopman, D., &Thompson, T. (1994). A descriptive study of physically aggressive behavior in dementia by direct observation. *Journal of the American Geriatrics Society*, 42(2), 192-197.

Burgio, L.D., Jones, L.T., Butler, F., & En Rel, B.T. (1988). Behavior problems in an urban nursing home, *Journal of Gerontological Nursing*, 14(1), 31-34.

Carmel, H., & Hunter, M. (1989). Staff injuries from inpatient violence. *Hospital and Community Psychiatry*, 40(1), 41-46.

Chou KR; Kaas MJ; Richie MF. Assaultive behavior in geriatric patients. *Journal of Gerontological Nursing*, 1996 Nov, 22(11):30-8.

Cohen-Mansfield, I. (7986). Agitated behaviors in the elderly: Preliminary results in the cognitively deteriorated. *Journal of the American Geriatrics Society*, 34(10), 722-727.

Cohen-Mansfield J. Assessment of disruptive behavior/agitation in the elderly: function, methods, and difficulties. *Journal of Geriatric Psychiatry and Neurology*, 1995 Jan, 8(1):52-60.

Cohen-Mansfield, I., & Billing, N. (1986). Agitated behaviors in the elderly: A conceptual view. *Journal of the American Geriatrics Society*,

34(10), 711-721.

Distasio, C.A. (1994). Violence in healthcare: Institutional strategies to cope with the phenomenon. *Health Care Supervisor*, 12(4), 1-34.

Durivage, A. (1989). Assaultive behavior: Before it happens. *Canadian Journal of Psychiatry*, 34(6), 393-397

Fornazzari i, Farcnik K, Smith I, et al. Violent visual hallucinations and aggression in frontal lobe dysfunction: clinical manifestations of deep orbito-frontal foci. *J Neuropsychiatry Clin Neurosci.*1992;4(1):42-44,

Frengley, I.D., & Mion, L.C. (1986).Incidence of physical restraints on acute general medical wards. *Journal of the American Geriatrics Society*, 34, 565-567-

Hatti, S., Dubin, W.R., Weiss, K.J.: A study of circumstances surrounding patient assaults on Psychiatrist. *Hospital & Community Psychiatry* 1982; 33:8.

J.R., Reid, W.H. (eds.): *Assaults Within Psychiatric Facilities*. New York: Grune & Stratton, 1983; 157-171.

Jacobs, D. (1983). Evaluation and management of the violent patient in emergency settings. *Psychiatric Clinics of North America*, 6(2),259-269.

Lanza ML. (1992) Nurses as patient assault victims: an update, synthesis, and recommendations. Arch Psychiatr Nurs. Jun;6(3):163-71

Lanza, M.L.: The reaction of nursing staff to physical assault by a patient. *Hospital and Community Psychiatry* 1983;34:1.

Miller RJ; Zadolinnyj K; Hafner RJ Profiles and predictors of assaultiveness for different psy-

chiatric ward populations. Dibden Research Unit, Glenside Hospital, Eastwood, *South Australia. Journal of Psychiatry* 1993 Sep;150(9): 1368-73

Negley, E.N., & Manley J.T. (1990). Environmental interventions in assaultive behavior. *Journal of Gerontological Nursing* 16(3), 29-33.

Phillips, P., Nasr, S.J.: Seclusion and restraint and prediction of violence. *American Journal of Psychiatry* 1983; 140:2

Poster, E.C., & livan, 1.A. (1989). Nurses' attitudes toward physical assaults by patients. *Archives of Psychiatric Nursing*, 3(6), 315-322

Rvden, M.B., Bossenmaier, M., & McLachlan, C. (1991). Aggressive behavior in cognitively impaired nursing home residents.

Rvden, M.B. (1988). Aggressive behaviors in persons with dementia who live in the community. *Alzheimer Disease and Associated Disorders* 2(4), 342-355.

Snyder W. III: Administrative monitoring of assaultive patients and staff in Lion, assault on health-care professionals. In J. Shepherd (Ed.), *Violence in health care* (pp. 1-11). New York, NY: Oxford University Press.

Tardiff, K., & Sweillam, A. (1979). The relation of age to assaultive behavior in inpatients. *Hospital & Community Psychiatry* (10), 709-710.

Treiman D (1986) Epilepsy and Violence: Medical and Legal Issues *Epilepsia* 27(suppl 2) S77-S104.

Weller P.G., Mungas, D., & Bemick,(1988). Popranolol for the control of disruptive behavior in senile dementia. *Journal of Geriatric Psychiatry & Neurology* 1(4), 226-:

Wisner, E., & Green M. (1986). Treatment of a